CW00435294

# THE WEIGH FORWARD

### Jules Williams

First published in 2011 by Quartet Books Limited
A member of the Namara Group
27 Goodge Street, London W1T 2LD

A catalogue record for this book is available from the British Library

ISBN 978 0 7043 7214 6

Typeset by Josh Bryson
Printed and bound in Great Britain by
T J International Ltd, Padstow, Cornwall

# Contents

Who Am I, And Why Did I Write This Book? 1

Introduction 3

    It is Time To Treat The Cause, Not The Effect 3

    Setting Off For An Arctic Expedition In Your Pants 5

    Know The Enemy 7

Before We Begin... 10

The Protection Factor 11

Sending A Positive Intent To Your Subconscious 15

Chapter 1 – The Subconscious 18

    The Grumpy Librarian Of Our Hard Drive 20

    Exercise: Your Story Begins 25

    Written Investigation 29

Chapter 2 – Emotional Correlation Timelines 30

    It's A Case Of Knowing What You're Looking For 30

    Exercise: The When and Where 31

        The When 31

        The Where 33

    Patterns, Glorious Patterns 35

    Exercise 39

Chapter 3 – Timings 40

    Timings for Weight / Body Conscious Actions 40

    Timings for Overeating or Drinking 41

    Exercise 42

Chapter 4 – Parts Of The Body 43

    The Belly / Tummy / Stomach 46

    The Back of the Arms 46

    The Chest / Breasts 46

    The Hips 47

    The Bottom 48

    Exercise 48

Chapter 5 – Chemotional Cocktails 51

    Exercise 54

Chapter 6 – The Connections Between Weight And Illness 55

    Exercise 59

Chapter 7 – Trigger Foods 61

Exercise 62

Chapter 8 – Mirrors: What Others Are Reflecting In You 65

 Exercise 66

Chapter 9 – The Language Of Weight Loss:The Power Of Your
  Words 68

 Exercise 72

 Exercise 73

 Exercise 74

Chapter 10 – Mothering And The Child Factor 76

 Exercise: For Women 78

 Exercise: For Men 78

Chapter 11 – The God Issue 80

 Exercise: Spiritual Visualisation 83

Chapter 12 – The Weight Of Abandonment 86

 Root Causes of Abandonment 88

 Exercise 88

 Exercise 89

Chapter 13 – 'Fat Is A Father Issue' 91

Chapter 14 – Chemotional Intelligence And Healing 94

 Emotional Release Pages 98

Chapter 15 – The Importance Of Ceremony 102

 Ceremony 1 104

 Ceremony 2 104

Chapter 16 – The Weight Of Responsibility: Dealing With
  Excuses And The Blame Culture 106

 Exercise 107

Chapter 17 – Repatterning And Reprogramming 109

 Affirmations 109

 Maximising Your Affirmations 113

 How To Say Affirmations 115

 When To Say Affirmations 116

 The Construction Of Affirmations 118

 Numerology 120

Chapter 18 – DNA And Energy Vibration 123

 Exercise 126

Exercise 128
Chapter 19 – Sticking Points 131
    Exercise 134
Chapter 20 – Habits, Patterns And Routines 135
    The Safe Sludge Syndrome 135
    Exercise 138
    Visualisations 138
    The Replacement Picture 139
    Exercise 141
    Intuitive Image Boarding 141
    Exercise: Creating Your Intuitive Image Board 143
Chapter 21 – Egregores And Understanding The Group
       Consciousness 145
    Exercise 147
Chapter 22 – Slimming Down Your Home And Slimming
       Down Your Shopping 148
    Items 148
    How And When You Shop 149
    Exercise 150
Chapter 23 – The Physical Level – Action 151
Chapter 24 – Confrontation 156
    The Main Confrontation 156
    This Is About You And Only You 158
    Steps To Narrowing Down Your Confrontation Focus 163
    Location 164
    Daily Confrontation 166
    Exercise 168
    Sneaky Subconscious Expectation 169
    Exercise 170
Chapter 25 – Spiritual Ego 172
    Is Your Job Or Your Role Keeping You Fat? 174
    Exercise 178
Chapter 26 – The Slimming Art Of Silence 179
Chapter 27 – Fat And The Food Industry 182
    Fat And The Frankensteining Of Food 184

Obesogens186
Medical Misconceptions187
Chapter 28 – Bulimia And Anorexia: The Emotional Causes192
Bulimia192
Anorexia193
Chapter 29 – Nutrition From The Inside Out195
Chemotional Understanding196
Water197
Food198
Chemotional Digestion199
Chapter 30 – Chemotional Pathways202
The Synergetic Link205
The Heart206
The Liver207
The Spleen208
The Kidneys209
The Lungs210
The Stomach212
The Small Intestine213
The Large Intestine213
Chapter 31 – Chemotional Exercise215
Chapter 32 – Chemotional Cleansing And Emotional Clearing
(Your Guided Visualisations Explained)218
Step 1 – Preparation218
Step 2 – Entering the Subconscious221
Step 3 – The Invitation222
Step 4 – The Catch-Up223
Step 5 – The Healing223
Step 6 – Cellular Release224
Step 7 – The Residues224
Step 8 – The Wash Through225
Step 9 – Reconnection and Re-affirmation225
Step 10 – The Return226
Chapter 33 – Simplicity From Complexity227

# WHO AM I, AND WHY DID I WRITE THIS BOOK?

This book and its exercises are the culmination of a lifelong observation, training and practical work. I say 'lifelong', because, almost from the start, I believed I could see the bigger picture of what was actually going on subconsciously in other people's lives. I am not your stereotypical psychic (for want of a better word). None of my family worked with their intuition, but were always very practical, logical and grounded - qualities that I grew up with. Keeping my intuitive abilities to myself, I got immersed in the physical world; growing up in the Welsh valleys, I played county rugby, ran the cross country for the Welsh national team, and played as many sports as there were hours in the day to be had.

I learnt from a very early age to manage my emotions and to fit in. Sport provided that outlet for me. I gained self-worth and confidence and, although I sensed I often knew the bigger picture of other people's emotional world, I kept it to myself. My physical understanding developed with a four-year honours degree in Physical Education, honing my teaching skills and physiological understanding. I also realised, like any fairly competent sportsman or woman, how powerful thoughts and mental toughness can contribute to better performance. Thoughts can actually be powerful – and have a relevance to whatever reality we create.

After graduating I moved to the USA where I coached soccer but, more importantly, committed to a life of spiritual understanding. Two years later, on returning to the UK, I gained spiritual healing qualifications and completed a three year intensive study of the subconscious. During this period, in the nineties, I remained active and became a black belt instructor of martial arts (a process which involved learning the philosophy of Zen *and* working with the subconscious).

I was also a personal fitness trainer, working with hundreds of clients and developing a modus operandi by looking at the whole of a person (Holistic) and how to help them move forward. In the mid-nineties I brought all this knowledge and understanding together with my intuition as an intuitive counsellor, helping clients clear deep-rooted emotional blocks from their life (and past lives) which were having a negative effect on their weight, relationships, addictions and health.

*The Weigh Forward* programmes that I developed as workshops, courses and individually with people, grew as a unique and all-encompassing approach. It dealt with the real reasons why an individual holds on to weight (or has developed an unhealthy attitude to food, image or their body shape). Over the last ten years I have showcased this information with regular television work, lectures, workshops, retreats and forums. I continue to push my investigations into the human psyche, subconscious and soul to reveal ever new levels of experience. This manual is both the fruition of my experiences and knowledge, but also my testament.

# INTRODUCTION

Around the world there are now one billion adults who are overweight. 320 million of them are obese yet the weight loss industry, with its £70 billion annual turnover, continues to systematically abuse the very people it claims to serve. Slimming groups, and the majority of diets, have a failure rate of up to 95 per cent with participants, often in despair at their own failure, regularly gaining even more weight in the long-term as the good intentions evaporate.

Obesity in children and adults has reached dangerously high levels and the sale of slimming pills, products and potions is a multi-million pound business bankrolled by sheer desperation. Millions of people are willing to spend their money on any new product which promises hope. Yet, as weight problems are still dangerously prevalent and the shocking statistics in my first paragraph prevail, the real answers to permanent weight loss are clearly not being found.

## It Is Time To Treat The Cause, Not The Effect

Most current approaches to weight loss fail because they tackle the problem from an over-simplified application of conscious reasoning. In other words, if you eat too much or eat the 'wrong' food, you get fat. *The Weigh Forward*, however, will deal with the subconscious root issues of weight gain, uncovering the reasons why we are really motivated to overeat or just unable to shift weight even if we manage to stick to a diet/exercise regime.

Many players in the weight-loss industry will attempt to offer their solution at the purely physical level (a process of diet and exercise) while others proclaim a more holistic solution (versions of psychotherapy / traditional counselling). Many try and override these blocked emotions with over-lays (hypnosis and NLP) but often never clear the root causes of the problem with their client. Any positive effects gained from these methods will only be short-lived. My book enables anyone to first recognise the causes and then sort them out, at the deepest level - inside out - so the weight-loss can be a lasting one.

People talk about comfort eating, instinctively recognising that, indeed, we do use food as a way to seek emotional sustenance. Yet there are no comprehensive or accessible guides providing the tools which can access our subconscious experience and clear the traumas which set up the patterning on an emotional level – until now, that is: by working on the principle that subconscious patterning, a process beyond our conscious control, sets up weight gain in the first place.

*The Weigh Forward* gives you the tools to recognise the emotional event that started weight gain, facilitate a change in the subconscious approach to that trauma and then re-pattern a much more positive connection to weight and food. By re-patterning our belief systems and thought processes, we change our subconscious reactions and, as a consequence, our bodies naturally and effortlessly let go of the excess weight and, as the root cause has finally been removed, the weight stays off.

In this book are tools garnered from twenty years experience in this field, including self-investigation, guided visualisations, emotional releasing techniques, journaling and dialoguing. This method of weight-loss from the inside out is a pioneering and definitive approach which addresses the emotional, mental, physical and spiritual causes of weight gain and facilitates lasting weight loss.

> '*To see your drama clearly is to be liberated from it.*'
>
> Ken Keyes Jnr.

*The Weigh Forward* is designed to help you understand the numerous and deep-seated reasons why your body may have been holding on to excess weight, and why your mind may be primarily obsessed with your weight, your body and your image. Reading this book and following the exercises will retrain your knowledge and heighten your intuition regarding your own emotional relationship with food and the shape of your body. (It is interesting that most of the people I have dealt with over the years, from all walks of life, will accept we are physical, emotional, mental and spiritual beings at the very least. It is not a leap of faith for most people to accept that, and yet we seem stuck in such a severely limited way of dealing with the issues of weight. People do try diets, maybe even delve into a bit of mind programming. But what happened to the belief that we are truly holistic beings?)

## Setting Off For An Arctic Expedition In Your Pants

If you go off on an Arctic expedition wearing only your underwear, you would be woefully underprepared and, regardless of all the willpower in the world, you would be setting yourself up for failure. You would also be underestimating your goal and not taking full advantage of the preparation and what is available out there to assist you. The same is true when embarking on a diet.

The question has to be raised that the current approaches to weight loss focus predominantly on a single word - and the extremely narrow focus of that word: DIET. You can look up a definition from any dictionary and all will make a reference to the association with food and physical shape.

This book is not going to guide you through the history of diets, or the type of diets that have been bandied around since the word hit a nation's consciousness, around 200 years ago. It is not going to regurgitate any number of so-called 'titbits of dietary information' which the internet will probably be storing in vast volumes, because this book is about taking you forward and finally offering the answers to lasting weight loss.

In a nutshell, more people than ever are going on diets. More money than ever is being spent on diets and more people than ever are overweight.
To me, the obvious conclusion is that DIETING MAKES YOU FAT.

The sad thing is that many people would recognise the truth of that statement, yet we are all fed by a media that constantly bombards imagery that continues to perpetuate the aforementioned and lucrative dieting market. Serious money means serious marketing!  Anyone who thinks that may be an overreaction should check out the combined wealth of the dieting industry.

These are the facts. Slimming organisations have, on average, a 95 per cent failure rate for long-term weight loss. It's obvious – of course they do – or by now, and all these marketing years later, they would have long ago been put out of business. We would be a nation of lean, fit, and healthy individuals. I have been racking my brains to see if there are any other businesses out there with such a massive failure rate, perversely making more money than ever, and - you know what - there may actually be one close contender: the pharmaceutical industry. Quelle surprise!

The upshot is, anyone who has struggled with a weight issue of whichever kind will want a quick fix answer and is usually habituated to try the usual suspects. Adding to that – as we have already mentioned – are the major financial players in the market and, before you know it, we're back on the merry-go-round of the dieting industry - deprivation, negative attitudes to food, pharmaceutical pills, potions and products, or even drastic invasive surgery.

I think the word 'sinister' is quite apt here. Individuals trying to deal with a weight issue are, in fact, having their vulnerability and desperation exploited by unscrupulous marketeers all too willing to offer the earth, and yet, in most cases, delivering only a small lump of turd.

Blame, though, is a useless emotion. It inhibits our ability to take responsibility. We should also recognise, especially in the last twenty years or so, the advent of the internet and of the beast that has become 'celebrity'. We have created a whole new zeitgeist to contend with which is subtly a further handing over of responsibility. Just because you can access information at the click of a button doesn't make it correct. Just because you continually see celebrity images doesn't make them a reality or quick fix goal (remember airbrushing and image manipulation?). The key dilemma, it seems to me, is that gradually, over time, people are losing the ability to trust their intuition for what feels right for them. There is so much distraction going on in the outside world that to think for oneself, to trust what feels right for oneself and to act for oneself, is becoming more and more difficult.

*The Weigh Forward* is actually a deeper process than you may have thought to begin with. It is about dealing with any weight issue from the inside out, rather than what I have high-lighted above – which tries to deal with it from the outside in.

Part of this book is a rediscovery of your own self. It does have a spiritual connotation and that is to recognise, by taking the time to take stock of what has actually gone on in your life and to understand what has shaped you, you will be able to hold yourself in good stead. Not just for dealing with your weight issues, but with your relationships, and many of the other challenges that life will throw at you.

## Know The Enemy

When I talk about working from the inside out, I mean working with yourself and looking at your emotions, and their associations with food and shape, as your initial investigation. Eve-rything that has been mentioned prior to this has all been external – different diets, dif-ferent pills, different products, different surgeries, or the outside influences of the celebrity image, of media advertising, or general media imagery in film and television. The female magazine industry and their online counterparts all only offer airbrushed or unrealistic physical imagery to sell or motivate desire. There is little understanding or, at least, honouring of the emotional debt behind the superficial façade. There is always duality to keep the subconscious tentatively oscillating between hurt and happiness.

This is one of the reasons diets have been able to keep being rebranded, either by exotic names to make us salivate at the lifestyle they are selling us (The South Miami Beach Diet) or by making a specific food group our enemy. To get together and fight against – like the carbohydrates in the Atkins Diet  (for the protein camp, low fat for another group, and so on). Another ploy is the individual case study; the 'I lost 40 lbs by eating grapes' or 'A bacon sarnie a day banished my gut'.

The same is true for celebrity-endorsed exercise videos. Vanessa Feltz must have made money out of her fitness regime, yet everyone appeared to miss the point. When she ended a long-term destructive relationship, the subconscious no longer needed to protect her from suppressed anger and any fears of being rejected. She could let go of the weight – and, of course, as soon as she was in a new relationship, and the same old subconscious patterns surfaced, she became heavier than ever before and seemingly forgot to mention her fitness DVD.

Anyone can think of an example of when they or a friend ended a relationship and had a dramatic change in weight. Just one example of there being deeper processes at work than mere nutrition and exercise – processes all to do with the subconscious, and a lifetime of individual patterning. Patterning which created certain fears, beliefs, and a way of emotional management (how we deal with painful emotions by suppression or trying to avoid experiencing them again).

# INTRODUCTION

The subconscious is actually not just the key to weight loss, but the holy grail of managing a more balanced life – by understanding your own subconscious quirks, traits and patterns and by clearing the negative ones,  you  can discern for yourself exactly what your body is reacting to (or trying desperately not to react to) and deal with it accordingly.

# BEFORE WE BEGIN...

## How To Use This Book

This is an interactive book for you to work through in the most clear and comfortable way that suits your learning and self-understanding.

You may choose to either:

1. Read the book first, then go back and work methodically through all the exercises and visualisations.
2. Read the book, stopping at each relevant place to work through the exercises and visualisations as they are presented.

Either way will be the perfect way for you. The important thing is your commitment to each challenge!

## The Tools Of This Book

There are two crucial components to assist you working through this book:

1. Your Journal. A writing book that you can use to privately participate in the exercises I give you. All the written exercises I specify should be done in here.
2. I have recorded your access to the Guided Visualisations to go hand-in-hand with the book's text. You can either download these visualisations for free at www.theweighforward.com/visualisations or enrich your experience of *The Weigh Forward* by downloading the sister Apps to the book in the iTunes store (search for Jules Williams – *The Weigh Forward*).

# THE PROTECTION FACTOR

Protection is probably the best word to describe how the subconscious uses our weight and body fat. Consciously, being overweight can make us unhappy on many levels, creating real and imagined restrictions in our lives. However, the subconscious uses the cushion of fat to protect us from suppressed emotions, self-loathing and as a physical buffer from the attention of others.

There are two main types of fat that we store within our bodies. Visceral is abdominal fat that is stored in the abdominal cavity, packed between the various organs (liver, kidney etc.) Subcutaneous is fat which is stored just below the skin.

Subcutaneous can be defined as situated under the skin, living in much the same manner as certain parasites. Suppressed emotions are literally parasitic feelings that have got under our skin. Physiological definition aside, on an emotional level it is interesting that both these terms are, in essence, clues to how our subconscious uses fat as protection. Visceral can also be defined as characterised by instinct or intuition, rather than intellect and also as dealing with base emotions, a raw emotional energy.

Fat, subconsciously, is doing exactly that – our subconscious uses fat to protect us from our raw emotions which are driven by our feelings and instinct as opposed to our being able to rationalise or intellectualise them.

Fat is the body's internal reaction to past traumatic events. The body is triggered to store fat (protection) when, at different times in our lives, we experience similar circumstances to

11

these root traumas.  Some examples of the emotional triggers for 'protective fat' are:

- Suppressing anger – because of the fear of being unloved or abandoned by the father and then subsequent male love relationships, any 'voice' for the self, which could in any way be construed as anger, gets suppressed. ('He won't love me and will reject me.')
- The suppressing of emotions of shame – because of a perceived shameful experience when younger (anything from serious abuse to being caught masturbating) uses weight as a protection from that shame, from feeling shame again or bringing shame on anyone else. It is exhausting and chemotionally destructive.
- Fear of not being loved, appreciated, liked or approved of – all emotions which are a result of low self-worth.
- Self-rejection, self-punishment, self-hatred – all the ways we can attack ourselves are painful emotions to experience, so end up getting suppressed under a protective cushion of fat.
- As a physical buffer from attention – in certain cases of abuse, inappropriate or hugely painful experiences, the subconscious uses weight as a protective barrier to prevent unwanted advances. ('If I'm big I won't get pestered.')

All the above can be seen as oversensitivity – a constant worry of what you can or can't say; of how you can or can't act; how others see you; what they feel about you. But it's exhausting and destructive.

The upshot is anyone carrying weight which they are unhappy or uncomfortable with will almost certainly have an underlying reason as to why. The reason will be a suppression of the specific emotions that create those chemotional cocktails and pathways within the body that assist the subconscious goal of holding on to weight as protection.

Physical efforts (diet and exercise) will remain sabotaged or ephemeral in nature until the subconscious reasons are recognised, cleared, healed and re-patterned.

Let's now look at a powerful example of 'protection' by the subconscious.

Janice, a forty-year-old mother of two, says she has struggled with weight most of her life. After embracing *The Weigh Forward* programme, she realised that her weight started when her parents got divorced when she was seven.

Janice loved her father but felt abandoned by him. She dared not get angry with him, in case he stopped seeing her on weekends and she lost him altogether. A pattern has been set up for Janice, *aged seven*, which, if one could actually 'talk' with her subconscious and ask what pattern was established, would go something like this:

*The pain of being abandoned by a male that I loved was too distressing emotionally and I never want that to happen again. So I will be as nice as possible to every male in my life and make them love me and then they will never leave.*

Aged seven, Janice thought that if she had been less trouble her dad would not have left home. In addition, she was often treated to sweets and chocolate by her late mother after the parental arguments – a third pattern for Janice's subconscious to 'work' with. So, already with her sixteen-year-old boyfriend and, indeed, all her major relationships, as soon as she was with someone her fear 'kicked in'. And the pattern of suppressing unwelcome emotions by eating sweets and chocolate began. Janice stopped being 'true' to herself – she doesn't dare get angry or ask for what she wants in case the man she loves leaves her.

So Janice continues with her life until, aged sixteen, she meets her first serious boyfriend and falls in love. Her subconscious checks back through its 'records', just like a computer searching for a match, and triggers emotions – her fear of being abandoned and doing everything possible to make the man love her and stay.

*The Weigh Forward* is a transformative and interactive book. It does require discipline, but only in the form of a willingness to look deeply at yourself and your life so far. It also requires you not to rush the process. To use an old cliché, this book is certainly about the journey – not the destination. If you take the time and fully embrace this journey then the destination of a balanced long-term weight loss will follow.

And your first commitment to this process must be made NOW!

# SENDING A POSITIVE INTENT TO YOUR SUBCONSCIOUS

Our contract is an important statement of intent, not only for the fact that writing something down increases your chances of success, but because, really, the narrative in this book is all about you and your willingness to move forward.

By committing to this process (on paper – or in your App) and with yourself, you are starting to recognise the importance of stating positive intent to your subconscious. The subconscious will only 'do what it's told' by repetition. Telling it that you are fat and one piece of chocolate will go straight to your thighs, sets the subconscious mind to work making sure that becomes reality.

The positive statements about you can start now.

Signature

CONTRACT:

'I _____ fully commit to *The Weigh Forward* Programme outlined in this book. I agree to engage as honestly as I can to the questions and investigations asked of me and devote the necessary time to all aspects of the programme. I am aware that all the questions have been deeply thought out by a professional and recognise that by skipping certain questions or by not devoting the necessary emotional time I may sabotage any success. During the six week process I will eat healthily and exercise regularly to compliment the mental, emotional and spiritual work *The Weigh Forward* entails.

Signed: _____

Date: _____

If you complete your contract you are not only ready to turn to Chapter 1 but you have also started the process of managing your thoughts from destructive and limiting to positive and limitless.

# 1

## THE SUBCONSCIOUS

*'Our subconscious minds have no sense of humour, play no jokes and cannot tell the difference between reality and an imagined thought or image. What we continually think about will eventually manifest in our lives.'*

Robert Collier

In order to explain the root causes of weight gain, it is important to understand the subconscious and show how powerful it can be in literally shaping our bodies as well as our futures. I refer to the conscious and subconscious, although they are not two minds, merely spheres of activity within one mind. The conscious is the reasoning mind, the place where we make all our choices and decisions. Conversely, it is our subconscious mind that automatically controls all the vital functions of our bodies such as our digestion, circulation and breathing, without any intervention from our conscious mind. It is the subconscious that throws up triggered emotions for us to contend with on a daily basis. Seemingly random thoughts, feelings and expectations are all spewed up from the obvious or innocuous triggers of interacting with daily life.

*'Programmers and marketing people know how to get into your subconscious – they spend millions of dollars researching colours, shapes, designs, symbols, that affect your preferences, and they can make you feel warm, trusting, like buying. They can manipulate you.'*

Richard Hatch

*'The conscious mind may be compared to a fountain playing in the sun and falling back into the great subterranean pool of subconscious from which it rises.'*

Sigmund Freud

There is a wealth of information available to us about the subconscious. Until recently it was usually the preserve of psychologists or philosophers. It's important that I stress here that I am not an advocate of clinical psychology or the numerous forms of psychotherapy. I deal with the subconscious, but I also deal with a human soul and its emotional patterning. I must also state that I am not a doctor, or a labelled academic. The understanding which I share in this book has been formed from my own studies and, for the last fifteen years, from working intuitively with thousands of clients.

It will be a common theme, as you begin to work with your 'self', that words themselves carry a certain power because of the judgements, labels, imagery and experience we associate with them during our own lifetime. For example, if I use the word 'orange' somebody may automatically trigger their five senses to smelling the tang of the orange fruit, the fizz of the taste, the feel of the waxy peel. Another person may be triggered to imagery of mobile phone providers or movie adverts. A veteran of Vietnam may well trigger negative thoughts of the US military's herbicidal warfare programme. Interesting then that to one person the word conjures up an appetising fruit and, to another, it may conjure up a poison that destroyed food.

The point being, when dealing with the subconscious it is how you build an internal computer programme of associations to certain words (thoughts, beliefs and feelings) which is the perfect opportunity to release judgements, labels and negative connotations with certain ones, starting right away with 'The Subconscious'. The subconscious is our super-computer. It is our internal hard drive which has stored every thought, experience, understanding, feeling, belief, image, emotion and sound which we have ever encountered since popping out of the womb – and also, for all our past lives too (If you don't believe in past lives, just associate the equivalent as cellular memory stored in your DNA from your ancestors.). That's the point: your subconscious has instant access to all this information.

## The Grumpy Librarian Of Our Hard Drive

What makes this grumpy librarian so interesting (and sometimes exasperating) to work with is that it wants to prevent us from experiencing a repeat of any trauma or suffering (Hurt), while trying to maintain its status quo of happiness. An obvious example, if you almost choke on a lollipop the trauma will make you avoid eating the same brand again. Conversely, somebody you love sharing a certain make of chocolate with, on romantic dates or at times of intimacy, will draw you back towards that same chocolate again and again. I use examples of food (this is the theme of this book after all), but where the subconscious creates a dichotomy or contradiction between 'hurt' and 'happiness', it creates what I call a negatively running virus in your internal hard drive.

A key example, and one I will cover in more depth later on, is that of male relationships with females. A little girl loves her father and experiences great happiness, feeling safe, secure and loved. But if her parents split up and the father leaves, rarely seeing his daughter, her subconscious will set up a negative virus. It will start to run a programme which will try and avoid feeling the suffering of being abandoned and feeling unloved. However, we are conditioned to search for a partner and to love, so the girl will have a continual cycle of going into relationships with men to feel loved, but will sabotage those relationships and end up repeating the suffering of abandonment over and over again. Her subconscious is stuck in the cycle of trying to avoid the hurt, but attempting to seek out happiness – the exact same conundrum as dieting cycles where positive and negative connotations are associated with food and eating, weight and body shape.

Dieting plays on the positive emotions associated with delicious food, treats and tickling those taste buds with other conflicting experiences: of bloating, punishment, deprivation and negative attitudes to certain foods.

The other important thing to realise with the subconscious is it's like our own garden. Everything we have ever seen, heard or experienced throughout our lives – every thought, observation, recognition, comment, experience and belief – becomes a seed. The subconscious mind is the fertile soil that accepts it – good or bad, positive or negative, true or false, common sense or nonsensical – and nurtures it into a plant or a weed. Whether we grow a patch of thistles or a multitude of fragrant flowers is down to the seeds which are sown in our subconscious. If we have negative, destructive thoughts, they continue to work negatively in our subconscious mind, ultimately creating an outer experience which reflects those thoughts and beliefs. For example, a woman who has had the early negative experiences of an abusive father and sees punishment as the way she can receive attention (love), can grow up to attract men with similar patterns of control and disrespect. Her subconscious belief is that she is worthless. A positive example of subconscious patterning is demonstrated by people who believe implicitly that they will never get ill. As a result, they rarely seem to catch the colds and viruses which are doing the rounds. As with all negative patterns rooted in the subconscious, weight loss needs to come from the inside out. No amount of trying to exert conscious control (like diet and exercise) is going to work until we work on a subconscious level. Get right back to the seed of the original weed – the emotional trauma which set up that belief pattern – uproot it, banish it and give our subconscious a new, positive seed to bring forth into reality.

Finally, however much I eulogise on our expansiveness and capacity for retaining information that is the preserve of the subconscious, it's important to realise that your own subconscious can be triggered or influenced by all of your senses. Not just sight, sound, touch, smell and feeling but by a nuance of thought, the subtlety of a place and a myriad of other fractions of peripheral experience. The scientist will refer to the subconscious mind and we will automatically relate to our brains but, in my experience as a lifelong intuitive, the subconscious resides in every single cell of our being *and* the 'space in-between'. It is imprinted on our energy fields (aura) and is probably the closest tangible link we have to our soul.

Each cell is a reflection of our whole and the many levels of our being.

*The Weigh Forward* is weight loss from the inside out. I have been working with my clients for the last twenty years helping them recognise that 'their thoughts create their reality'. Thankfully, this is a message which has slowly started to sink into the nation's consciousness too, with certain spiritual information now becoming more mainstream. The reality is that our thoughts do create what we consider reality. It all works from the inside out. Our physical bodies are merely a reflection of our thoughts and emotions, and the more charged with emotions our thoughts are the more our physical bodies will respond. (It can't work the other way round.) By saying repetitively: 'food goes straight to my hips'; 'I can't even look at chocolate without putting weight on'; 'I'm so fat'; 'I'm so weak willed when it comes to food!' and numerous other statements I have heard from my clients over the years, just means the sub-conscious is working overtime to manifest reality. Remember the power of these statements is amplified depending on the amount of highly charged emotion behind it. I have heard many slim people say, 'I'm so fat.' But what their friends don't hear is the silent voice in their minds: 'I'm actually really slim. I'm fit and healthy.' Don't confuse the two.

If you say certain statements, check how emotionally charged they are for you but also check what your silent thoughts are *after* you have spoken.

> '*Your experience in the world of physical matter flows outward from the centre of your inner psyche – then you perceive this experience. Exterior events, circumstances and conditions are meant as a living feedback. Altering the state of psyche automatically alters the physical circumstances.*'

Seth Speaks

> '*By choosing your thoughts, and by selecting which emotional currents you will release and which you will reinforce, you determine the quality of your Light. You determine the effects that you will have upon others, and the nature of the experiences of your life.*'

Gary Zukav

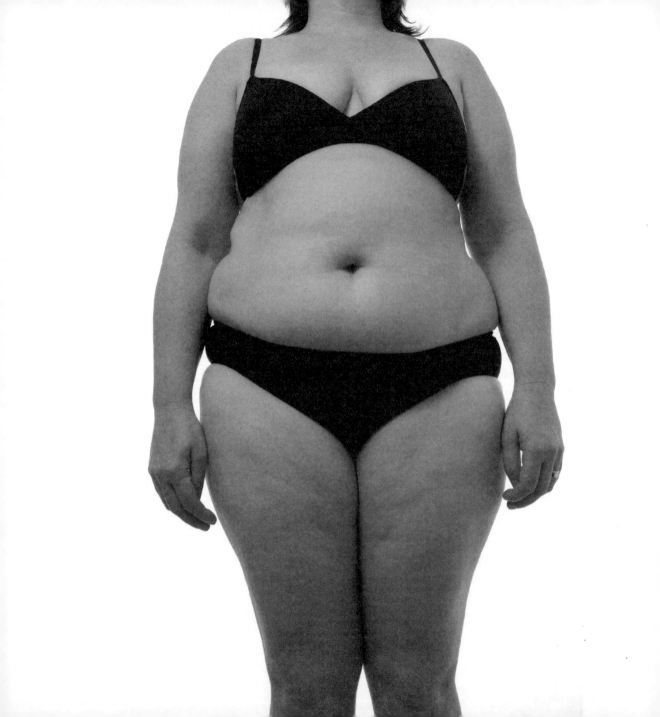

## Exercise: Your Story Begins

The key to *The Weigh Forward* is weight loss from the inside out. The first place we start is to look at your external body and delve into the thoughts and emotions that have been attached to weight and specific areas of your body. It's really important that you get a photograph taken of you – you and your body. This is an investigative exercise and it is the internal dialogue that is important. All that is needed is a clear full-length body photo, naked if you are brave enough or in plain underwear if not.

You have to feel totally safe that the only person who is going to see this photograph is you, and so it's a good time to decide on where you are going to keep your *The Weigh Forward* Journal for the duration of this programme. This may sound unnecessary to the singleton reading this book who says, 'It's fine on my bedside table.' But people who live in busy households with nosey flatmates, cheeky children or controlling husbands and partners may already have alarm bells ringing in their minds.

This is more than just about a photograph for, during this process, emotional traumas or events from your past may be explored and unearthed in order to recognise and heal. It requires bravery to be honest, even with yourself, on paper, and it is imperative you are honest during *The Weigh Forward* programme – but it is vital that you are secure in the knowledge that you have safety and privacy for your *The Weigh Forward* Journal.

But coming back to the photograph. With today's technology, some of you may already have taken a picture on your digital camera, uploaded it to your computer and printed it out. Others, perhaps, on their mobile phones and are already printing it out at Boots. The point is not about having a portrait taken to 'gallery standards', but a clear image for you to work with, practically. What you may find interesting, as with every interactive process of this book, is that the subconscious will try to sabotage your efforts.

For example: 'I'll have to wait until I finish the film before I develop it' (which ends up being after next year's summer holiday); or, 'I'll wait for my girlfriend to come back next week and she can take it'. There are any number of other delays and excuses. However plausible they seem, ask yourself are you making this a priority? If not, how low down on the list of priorities is it? Also, keep a note of all the worries you have around taking pictures – remember, if you have struggled with weight you have most likely made a camera your enemy, and will have all manner of tactics to avoid having your picture taken. But once you have:

- Look at the photograph of yourself and describe what you see. This process should take a minimum of 20 minutes. You are aiming to bring to the surface all the associated thoughts and emotions you have about yourself. Write all of them down, however dark, flippant, emotional or humorous they may be. Include any facet at all of your body, your shape, your image and your perceptions.
- Look at your picture, scan through the different parts of your body and write down what you feel about them. It may be because of fat, because of shape, because of what someone has said or implied about that part of your body. It may be because it reminds you of an illness, or an accident, birthmarks, or it may be because of being told it reminds a parent of 'your father's legs' and some other part of someone else's anatomy. There may be previous comments from family, friends, peers, work colleagues or even judgements made in magazines or on television. It may also remind you of abuse in some way.

When you feel you have exhausted the comments and descriptions, take a three minute breather – walk around the house, put the kettle on – by yourself, though don't break the energy by making phone calls or talking to others. Come back to the picture and start again. Often deeper feelings surface if you keep up this process. Repeat at least three times before being satisfied that all the information has surfaced. (You will be coming back to the photograph at the end of *The Weigh Forward* process too.)

Freya (aged thirty-six) initially studied her photograph and focused on the usual aspects of tummy and hip fat. Eventually she remembered an incident when she was twelve when a male family friend had patted her bottom and jokingly commented on how slim and firm it was. Her own experience of this (it is really important to recognise that every individual has different reactions and emotions in similar situations) was feeling very self-conscious and that all the family looked at her. It wasn't a feeling of discomfort at the act, but the fact she felt everyone watching her and blushing, without knowing what to say. The subconscious from that moment set up a fear of being put on the spot or in the spotlight, if she were slim and fit. That was a key event for her subconscious, and weight became a protection from having to speak up for herself. Freya, through following *The Weigh Forward* programme, could then recognise times in her life – such as performing monologues at school and university, sales presentations at work or giving the eulogy at a friend's funeral – when she could literally 'put a stone on overnight'; a wonderful example of how seemingly innocuous events can set up direct relationships to weight and body image.

Jody was looking at her photograph and, similarly to Freya, made the usual self deprecating comments about fat around her tummy and hips, but became quite emotional later on looking at a scar she had down her right front shoulder and off to the side of her breast. She had been knocked over by a car when she was ten and, although that was a major trauma in itself, the way it related to weight explained a lot more for her. Her mother had always blamed her, insinuating she hadn't been looking where she was going ('daydreaming Jody') just before the accident. She instinctively knew it hadn't been her fault, but because she had little memory of the event she couldn't speak up for herself. Over the years Jody has become very controlling in her behaviour, constantly trying to avoid a repeat of being judged a 'daydreamer' and in any circumstance in her life when she feels she is being judged she overeats. Her weight was because of suppressed anger at not being taken seriously, the subconscious creating a cushion of fat from that anger. As a double whammy, she subconsciously felt that if she was overweight she could hide her shoulders under larger clothes so didn't have to see the reminder of her 'stupidity' with the scar. All of that suppressed emotion and pattern with weight started to come to light and give Jody the chance to lose it, because of the very first exercise of deeply scrutinising the photograph of her physical body.

Alex was delving into his photograph, and hated his arms. The emotions were very powerful and logically made little sense as his arms were normal looking. Aged 13 at school (he incidentally went to the same school as his father) his P.E. teacher had said he would be good at discus throwing because he had his father's arms and 'chunky' physique. Alex hated his father (he had suffered physical abuse and insults all his life) and so throughout school stayed slim and avoided the throwing events at all costs; a way of not having to be like his father. This subconscious anger and weight problem was really triggered on his wedding day. He vividly remembers being told by his mother, as he headed off on his honeymoon just after the wedding, 'Take care of her, son; you are the man of the house now.' To Alex's subconscious this was a massive realisation of a fear he had been avoiding his whole life – by being a husband and now the man of the house he (to his subconscious) had just become his father.

Alex had two weeks in Malta for his honeymoon and put on three stone in weight. I have seen this numerous times with people involved in *The Weigh Forward* programme, where dramatic weight gain or weight loss at times in their life confirms much deeper reasons than mere calorific intake and exercise. Alex laid down the cushion of fat against emotions of self-hatred. (He hated

28

his father, so to the subconscious by associating him as being his father he had to hate himself by default.) For the next ten years before embarking on the programme, Alex followed his father's pattern – Alex left his wife, and became a similarly absent father.

## Written Investigation

1.  Make a list of the main foods and food groups in your life so far, and note alongside any emotional events which are attached to those foods, any positive or negative experiences, and/or any other habits connected with those foods. For example, one of my clients remembered that each time she had to go away on school trips her mother made ham and cucumber sandwiches for her. She hated leaving home and recognises even now, when she feels on her own, she will make ham and cucumber sandwiches.
2.  Make a list of the statements you have made in your life about certain foods or your body weight / shape (however embarrassing).
3.  Make a list of the emotional words you have used with regard to food and body weight / shape. For example, one of my clients recognised that her subconscious would hold on to her food because it triggered responding to being starving and needing to stock up, and so would sabotage the effects of exercise, to keep the weight on.

# 2
## EMOTIONAL CORRELATION TIMELINES

### It's A Case Of Knowing What You're Looking For

The subconscious stores full and complete records of all aspects of our lives. As you investigate and try to understand your issues with food / weight and body image, it helps to clearly map out the key events and subsequent triggers that have occurred over your life. It's amazing how many of my clients, over the years, are so vague about what was going on in their lives when they first put on weight, because we are so conditioned to think in physical terms. ('What was I doing?' refers to our actions, as opposed to the most important realisation: what was going on emotionally. Instead of 'What was I doing?' it is more a case of, 'What was I feeling?')

It's about looking at those areas of your life which trigger strong emotions. Two of the main areas are relationships and events (relationships with family, friends, peers, teachers, co-workers; strangers and events that are traumatic and painful for you). For example, many of the clients who had started off saying nothing much was going on when they first put on weight suddenly came up with core emotional events when mapping out their emotional correlation timelines with their own weight 'history'.

Andrea put on a lot of weight initially when she was eleven, when she entered a new class and was being bullied; Chloe had a pregnancy scare at fifteen and Sarah moved house to a street where none of her friends lived. I pick a few examples so that you can understand that weight is a 'protection' for our subconscious and a protection from issues of self-worth, from suppressed anger, from fear of being abandoned and many other conflicts. It is only when such events become obvious that we begin to understand what is happening to us. Before understanding this, Andrea, Chloe and Sarah had been oblivious to each event's significance.

## Exercise: The When And Where

Having scrutinised your photograph and self-investigated, through the writing exercises and digesting the previous case studies, these new exercises will continue the process of unravelling the core events that have shaped your body's reactions to your emotional past.

## The When

You will be increasingly aware now that the subconscious is the key to understanding weight loss, and that the patterns you have been running within your subconscious have set up a 'need' to hold on to weight for protection from certain emotions. To clear these patterns it is important to recognise and clear the root event – the core experience which triggered your subconscious from the very start and set up its destructive rationale around weight. The first stage of this is to  work with your *The Weigh Forward* timeline. On the next page of your *The Weigh Forward* Journal draw a basic line graph where the horizontal line holds the increasing values for your age from zero, on the left, to your current age, on the right. On the vertical axis, draw values for weight in stone, again from zero to your maximum weight.

In your Journal draw a time-line mapping out your age from birth to the present day and marking out significant weight gains and weight losses in your life. Because the root causes of weight are emotional, if you cast your mind back to what events and feelings were present at those times of weight change and note what was going on with family / relationships / personal circumstances, your specific subconscious associations will be revealed.

These events reveal the triggers that the subconscious aligns with the times it needs to protect (store fat) and times when it feels safe and can let go of weight.

Some examples of relationship traumas that have instigated my client's weight gain:
- A parental  argument / split / divorce / infidelity / abuse / depression / illness
- A death of parent / grandparent / sibling / friend
- Personal conflict with another person in terms of bullying / abuse / competition / deception / mistrust / theft / jealousy / sibling being born / sibling rivalry / personality clash with a teacher or other person

Some examples of events that have instigated my client's weight gain:
- Being left in hospital by parents when ill as a child
- Moving house, moving school, emigrating, immigrating
- Witnessing a parent having an affair or being intimate
- Having to cope with a depressed parent or an ill parent
- Having a disabled sibling requiring constant care
- Having a serious accident
- Destructive holiday or school trip, or any travel away from home where something happens or has happened while you are away and is only discovered when you return
- Experiencing a miscarriage or a termination
- An embarrassing event such as being laughed at on stage or having a secret revealed about you by someone whom you trusted

The above examples are to help guide you as to the types of relationship or event triggers that have affected other people. They are only examples; what gets logged as an emotional event, and then relates to food and weight by the subconscious is individual.

Explore all the minutia of the emotional interactions and / or events of your main weight peaks and troughs.

In the diagram, Rachel first put on a noticeable increase in weight when she was seven and suffered from feelings of rejection and abandonment when her father left. She was sixteen when her first serious boyfriend broke up with her. Her weight stabilised when she married as she felt secure. When she divorced, all the compounded suffering of losing male love pushed the weight up once more.

## The Where

Answer the following questions:

1. Where on your body do you predominantly feel you carry weight (including the most easily stored areas, or the most stubborn areas to shift it from)?
   - Where were you living when you first put on noticeable weight – and where were you living when you subsequently, in your life, put on notice-

able weight? (Include location, distance from friends and family, whether you were in or out of a relationship, living with parents, parents going through a divorce, you were married, splitting up.)

- Where were you in your life when you put on weight? Changing schools, leaving schools, moving away to university, starting a job, getting pregnant, going through a career change, in or out of a relationship, suffering a loss of a loved one.

2. After answering the questions, pick the example you feel most emotional about and complete three pages of stream of consciousness writing. Any time you complete stream of consciousness writing during *The Weigh Forward* process, keep the pen moving at all times, write a minimum of three pages of A4 and keep referencing what you are writing back to what you are feeling now and what you were feeling then.

Remember, this is an emotional process centred on feelings from the past and powerful emotions that are triggered in the present. It is not an exercise in logical understanding by your intelligent adult self. Even if you are writing a few sentences along the lines of 'this is a load of baloney, I don't really know what I am writing, anyway where was I, oh yes what *was* I actually feeling when I was dropped off that first day of boarding school' it is very important to keep the pen moving.

To recap, you have started the valuable process of recognising that not only are there deeper underlying issues with your weight, shape and body image but exactly, like a jigsaw, you are now beginning to fit the picture of your life-connected-to-weight together.

All stages of your own investigation and healing with *The Weigh Forward* are relevant. To complete the deep subconscious visualisations and powerful affirmations that are revealed in the later chapters will add to what you have achieved already.

## Patterns, Glorious Patterns

Once you have the main emotional correlations logged with specific times of weight gain and weight loss, I want you to start to think how the subconscious works so you can understand your pattern. That is the thing about the subconscious. It can find a good place to file everything if it can fit into a pattern. Remember, it recognises and logs everything. So, for example, if you experienced an emotional trauma by being bitten by a dog while walking in the local park, you would imagine your subconscious would just help you avoid the local park as it obviously wants to protect you from experiencing that trauma again. But hold on, for the subconscious is far more thorough than that!

You would start to feel twitchy walking anywhere where there are dogs. You would unconsciously start avoiding places where dogs are walked. You'd be triggered into feelings of unease seeing a dog on television. You would find yourself walking more and more in crowded areas where dogs are on a tight leash. You may even find you more often go out with a partner or a friend and less on your own. A whole host of subtle dog avoidance strategies would spring from your subconscious.

And that's just the start of how your subconscious would respond. If, for example, you had just started your menstrual cycle the day you were attacked, years later you may feel uneasy on the first day of your cycle and have no idea why. If you had just so happened to have been worrying about paying a bill that morning, subconsciously, in the future, you would be twitchy around similar feelings and again not know why.

Not underestimating the subconscious is so important and why, once you have highlighted the key emotional correlations you have with weight, you can play detective around what it means to the subconscious.

I have developed with my clients a three-point understanding when undergoing this subconscious investigation.

1. The Root Event (your core emotional block) – the first emotional situation that set up a destructive association with food, weight and body shape.
2. The Triggers – associated situations which hold a similar emotional response as the initial root event.
3. The Associations – the daily interactions which the subconscious responds to, to protect you from feeling the destructive emotions.

Below are a few examples of some of my clients' root events, triggers and associations:

| Roger (46) | |
|---|---|
| Root Event | His mum miscarried when he was three and he took the responsibility for her suffering. |
| Triggers | Taking the responsibility for her pain, he became her 'little helper', which then got transposed by his subconscious on to his girlfriends and wife. Their needs became more important than his. He needs permission to do things for himself from a lack of confidence in his own decisions if they are not based around helping females. There was a double whammy with Roger as his dad was jealous of his son's relationship with his mum. ('Get to school you little shit.') Roger felt small and worthless, reinforcing his pattern of needing to be told what to do. His dad took power – and Roger got fat; his weight his protection from being small - a 'little shit'. |
| Associations | Would find himself eating if he bought something or did anything for himself (to suppress his feelings of guilt for not helping females) but also if he felt that someone had not heard or listened to him (insignificant) |

| Karen (29) | |
|---|---|
| Root Event | Aged seven, her mother blamed her chronic arthritis on Karen being born. |
| Triggers | Karen assumed the caretaker role of her mother and all the female friends in her life. The constant stress of doing everything for them and trying to make them happy (still really the fearful little girl scared of not being loved by mum, and trying to prove it was worth her being born because she is such an invaluable help). |
| Associations | Puts a brave face on her own feelings as scared of upsetting her mum, and considering what her mum had to sacrifice. Her friends are her subconscious extension of her mum. Dairy is a big trigger food, as nurturing anxiety creates the extra weight going on her breasts and tummy, as she 'self-mothers' and feels denied love/nourishment. (It would have been better if she wasn't born – because she was, though, she must make it up to her mum and every other female.) |

| Nicola (27) | |
|---|---|
| Root Event | She almost died in an accident aged seven. She felt she would lose her family and all their love if she had died and felt very lonely. |
| Triggers | Any time people aren't in her sight or she isn't with people, she eats to suppress her feelings of loneliness. She needs to be around others to feel safe and protected. Puts weight on as a protection in her life when she doesn't have a partner or is not in job or not around friends. |
| Associations | Any time during the day when she isn't with someone or can't get hold of them on the phone, she eats to suppress her loneliness and fear. |

## Exercise

Make a note of what you are now beginning to understand as:

- Your Root Event (your core emotional block)
- Your Triggers
- Your Associations

# 3

## TIMINGS

Once you have recognised and cleared the root event (Core Emotional Block Visualisation – Chapter 32) which set up the pattern of weight gain and holding on to weight, part of the earlier exercises were also to understand your pattern and the types of major shifts in your life which can trigger these big fluctuations. It is also very revealing to be conscious of the more subtle indications that you will deal with on a daily basis. I've explained earlier how your experiences in the world are a reflection of your thoughts and emotions, and if you pay attention to the minutiae of your daily life, such events can reveal much of what is going on.

In this section, you will be looking to break down your daily routines and habits to reveal where the windows to what you are feeling or thinking are expressed, and also what the so-called 'danger zones of timings' are during your day / week or monthly cycles.

### Timings For Weight / Body Conscious Actions

All clients who follow *The Weigh Forward* find that they have a time (or numerous times) throughout the day when they pay attention to their weight or an area of their body. This can be in the form of unconsciously touching a fat part of their bodies repeatedly. It could be an action of jumping on the scales first thing in the morning, or after getting out of the shower at night. It could be putting themselves down in front of others about their weight.

Here are a few examples some of my clients revealed:

- Beth always rubs her thumb over her belly and 'love handles' when she eats food (the body is associating all food with going to her waist).
- Kathy pulls her t-shirt or jumper down over her bum every single time she stands up, 'so no one sees the size of it'.
- Jackie unconsciously crosses her hands over her chest when talking to men, 'so they don't ogle my boobs.' (It was such a habit she didn't realise she was doing it.)
- John always weighed himself on a Saturday morning, convinced that 'the Friday night out I enjoyed is going to punish me with extra pounds.' (His dad used to call him a waster on Saturday mornings after he enjoyed himself as a teenager on Friday nights.)

These examples tell a story (all of them only realised by doing the timings investigation). To help break the habit and prevent the negative pattern to the subconscious, they could attempt to catch themselves doing the physical things they do and try to be easy on themselves about the underlying thought and feeling behind their actions. So John stops weighing himself on a Saturday morning and begins to take it easy on himself for having had a good time (perhaps he thoroughly deserved it). Kathy can try to stop the habit of pulling down her jumper and might stop repeating those negative thoughts that affirm the size of her bottom.

## Timings for Overeating or Drinking

- Where are your danger zones for overeating or for eating certain types of food?

- Do you eat most of your food at night once you relax and your working day is over?
- Do you have a lonely mid-afternoon slump, and that's when cake and biscuits are eaten?
- Is it after the kids have been dropped off for school?

It's very telling to see what times during the day are your 'danger zones'. There will be an underlying subconscious reason why you are drawn to eat particular foods, or are in a pattern of craving food at certain set times. For example, as a child, Wendy was left alone by her parents from around five o'clock every evening. In adulthood, her subconscious views the evenings as a period of abandonment and loneliness. As a consequence, she has developed a pattern of eating very little during the day but, in her words, 'making a fattering meal and polishing off a bottle of wine every evening'.

## Exercise

Create a timetable of your typical day from when you usually wake up to when you go to sleep and, acting on the information above, from the two categories of timings / windows during the day, log what times are your own personal habits and exactly what kind of body awareness, action or food consumption or craving they are.

Don't worry if it is not fully clear to you why you do these things, as at present you are in the process of building the complete picture for yourself.

# 4

## PARTS OF THE BODY

By now you will have started to realise how both your internal and external worlds will always reflect what is going on in your life and what needs addressing. When I mentioned earlier that people might misjudge the subconscious mind as being solely part of a sphere of the brain, it is to miss the point. The subconscious is manifest in every single cell of your being and throughout all the energy centres of your being. When I discuss the advances in understanding your DNA, because of this interconnectedness, I was made very aware over the years that even particular areas of the body where you hold on to extra weight are associated with specific emotions. If you do have a specific area of your body that you feel is the most susceptible to putting on weight, or an area which you spend most of your time focusing on or worrying about, there will certainly be a reason for whatever negative emotions the subconscious is attempting to protect you from and will use as a cushion made from fat.

43

It is so important to wake up to the fact that extra weight, in the form of storing body fat, is because of an underlying emotional cause. You could go as far as to say that it is the naivety of old conditioned thinking to think that your shape is only a consequence of what you eat or what exercise you do.

You are not what you eat by any stretch of the imagination!

You are actually a complex reaction of what you eat, what you are feeling, what you are thinking and what you are experiencing. You have also had a lifetime of conditioning tied to beliefs that have been set up around food within your physical, mental, emotional and spiritual body.

So what is actually going on in the storing of body fat on an emotional level? Well, because of the root event that set up your pattern, the subconscious is trying to prevent you from experiencing the pain, vulnerability and trauma of that experience again. In essence it is suppressing what I call 'triggered emotions' (emotions that are similar to the root event you experienced but not as powerful).

Extra weight / fat is seen by the subconscious as protection, cushioning you from the pain of those emotions. People have not been taught to understand that everything carries energy and if, for example, someone is feeling angry but never venting or expressing that anger, the energy behind it has to go somewhere, and that somewhere could be suppressed and stored in the body. The same applies for destructive feelings about the self.

People who struggle with weight often say, 'I completely understand that for myself, but how come my husband has a similar issue going on and he's like a bean pole?' An excellent point, and being an intuitive person, I usually answer back very specifically about the person they are talking about. With this woman it was, 'OK, how come your husband will never have enough money to buy the things he wants? He earns good money and gets everything for the family and the home but every time he tries to save for something an unexpected bill comes in or work dries up or someone in the family needs something. Do you think that is just coincidence or, like understanding weight, do you think there may be underlying subconscious issues going on?'

Of course there is more going on. It is just that where one person has their subconscious pattern latch onto associations with food and weight someone else's subconscious may latch onto associations with money and paying for things. Food, money and relationships are the usual suspects because these are something we are exposed to numerous times every day and are all integral parts of our life. They are so easy to condition too.

Below are a list of patterns that have emerged with my clients over the years relating to the emotional correlations to those specific parts of the body which are storing fat.

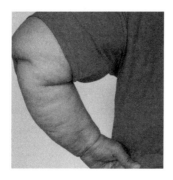 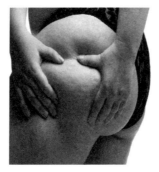 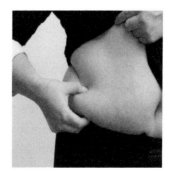

## The Belly / Tummy / Stomach

I have found that when the focus is on the belly, it's because the person is angry. They feel they're doing everything for everyone else but no one is doing anything for them. They are in a pattern of always giving and not receiving so the subconscious rectifies this neglect by 'self-nourishing' and weight is kept on the place which the subconscious associates with the area where we receive our vital nourishment: the stomach. People can pinpoint exactly when they feel bloated or are carrying extra weight in this area with peak periods of nourishing everyone else but themselves. The fat is protection from suppressed anger and subconsciously feeling worthless (if you are doing everything for everyone else and not yourself then the subconscious thinks everyone is more important than you and, by default, you are worthless).

## The Back Of The Arms

The triceps, or the back of the arms area, is really interesting too. It relates to an anger of being denied love; subconsciously, the extra weight pushes the arms out from the body as if the person is asking for a hug, creating a visual cry for love as the person is unable to verbalise this need. Although in some cases there can be only extra weight in this area, it is often when a person is carrying lots of extra weight all over their body but the back of the arms is still very obvious. There will be either a very upsetting past of adoption or foster homes or a father who only lives for his sons and ignores his daughter, or parents who were blatantly abusive (mentally, emotionally or physically) and the person has shut down from expecting any kind of love. Such suppression is literally trying to push them into the arms of another person.

## The Chest / Breasts

The chest or breasts of a person represent emotions associated with mothering. Claire had a size 34B chest and a mother who doted on her. Within six weeks of moving away from her mum to university, Claire's bust size increased to 36D with no weight gain elsewhere. The subconscious had 'self–mothered'; Mum wasn't around so the mothering area of the body compensated.

Never underestimate the power of the subconscious and its emotional associations. If some-one is literally mothering everyone else, either with their physical children or with their friends, colleagues and family, and their own mother was absent physically or emotionally, they can put weight on in this area. It is a safe bet if someone has large breasts they have issues with their mother in some way. This is also just as applicable to men too.

NB – it is interesting to note that, in my experience, most of the women in the 'glamour' industry have 'daddy' issues. There's also a subconscious drive from them to overly mother as they have in essence been abandoned by their father (physically or emotionally) and also to try and attract approval and attention from men (father love). The need to be needed by men is so strong, though, because of the childhood abandonment, that their subconscious hasn't got time to be mothering everyone else. So, hey presto, they have to artificially inflate their breasts.

## The Hips

The hips relate to an area that is akin to 'stubborn lumps of anger'. The fat stored here is sup-pressed anger which the person is stubbornly refusing to let go of. The hips also relate to the stabilising part of our skeleton and, hence, too much weight here is destabilising and out of balance. It could be that you are being a little too hard on other people, either through gos sip or behaviour. Don't give yourself a hard time. Just use it as an opportunity to see that maybe some anger you have had no longer serves you and, difficult as it is to let go, a little bit of wounded pride is a small price to pay for letting go of the past.

## The Bottom

The bottom is actually linked to a deep-seated fear of death. Quite often there is a negative block from a past life where the subconscious thinks it has been let down by 'God' or is going to be punished. In this life the loss of a loved one or even something as innocuous as watching a movie which shows death as religious punishment, is enough to trigger the subconscious. The subconscious is actually trying to weigh you down, to stop you from moving forward – because the ultimate place we move forward to is through life and towards death.

It is as though the subconscious thinks, if it can hold you back, it can delay that punishment or rejection by God. All the suppression of our sometimes irrational fear gets stored in this area. If you look at different cultures around the world, the fire and brimstone religious ones will have, in many cases, issues with weight in this area – think of the Deep South in the USA.

## Exercise

- Using the diagram below, shade the area where you feel you hold on to weight. The area where weight usually goes on first and comes off last – it is fine if there is more than one area of your body. Just be sure to take each individual area one at a time when delving deeper.
- From reading about the different areas above, write down:
  - Why you feel you are holding weight in that area?
  - At what times do you put on or lose weight in that area?
  - What standard sayings do you have to describe that area of your body (to yourself or others)?
  - How often do you look negatively at that area, touch that area and also think negative thoughts about that area? Make a note of how often in any 24-hour period.

- Do you go to special efforts when dressing to disguise, accentuate or draw attention away from that area? To what extent are your clothes and your style affected by that area?

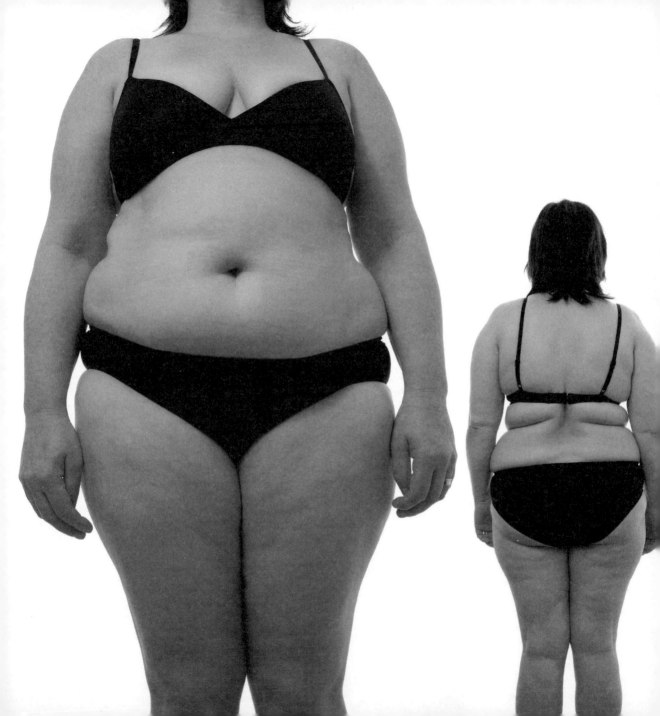

# 5

## CHEMOTIONAL COCKTAILS

It is scientific fact that emotions release hormones and create chemical reactions in the body and that all this happens at a subconscious level. A well known example is when in a fight or flight situation, adrenaline is produced, making us more alert and giving us the stamina to either physically defend ourselves or flee a dangerous situation for our survival.

It is also scientific fact that our foodstuffs are produced with, or naturally contain a plethora of chemicals, as do pharmaceutical drugs (of course). It is our subconscious which controls the absorption, ingestion and assimilation of that food and the chemicals within. Specific emotions and their subconscious associations with weight will determine whether your body produces a mixture that will slow down digestion and absorption and 'protect' you with fat, or speed up the assimilation process so your body doesn't hold on to extra weight. For example, if someone is emotionally fearful of rejection, this releases particular chemicals into their body which will have a unique reaction to the chemicals in their food. The subconscious is controlling the 'chemotional cocktail' to slow down the system, digestion and absorption, and predispose that particular person to hold on to more fat.

You can't control the absorption, ingestion and assimilation of food on a conscious level, i.e. by trying to change food groups, take pills, have injections etc., because the subconscious, NOT THE CONSCIOUS, controls all vital functions. Any attempt to control the body for more than a limited time through external means vastly underestimates the power of the subconscious mind. Whether the person sabotages and 'falls off the diet wagon', or they need to keep upping the strength of their medical dosage, or they crave or react to certain foods, is all because they have to work with their emotions alongside their eating.

Everybody has examples of someone they know who eats 3,000 calories a day of junk food, does little exercise and loses weight and someone who lives on a meagre 1,100 a day of 'healthy' foods and gains weight.

It's not what you eat, it's the way you EMOTE it!

*The Weigh Forward* clears the blocked subconscious emotions which are being triggered, enabling a return to chemical balance within the body. This in turn stops the individual being attracted to certain food groups and ensures they are eating from a point of balance. For example, eating bread from a positive emotional balance, which will release non-reactionary chemicals as opposed to eating bread when feeling worthless, which prompts the release of antagonistic chemicals and predisposes the body to hold on to fat.

And the subconscious really struggles when it has the hurt/happiness continuum going on. Where it is drawn to wanting something it perceives would be pleasurable for you (a loving relationship) but is trying to stop you experiencing the traumatic emotions again (a rejection of love in a relationship). All this correlates with the chemical reactions and 'chemotional cocktails' zipping around your system.

The word is stress – that bland, all-encompassing, not really telling you anything, word. Doctors love it; if they can't be specific they just use the standard get out of jail free card and call it stress. *The Weigh Forward* is about breaking down stress into specifically understood reactions to specifically understood thoughts and emotions which every individual will have triggered at certain times. For example, Sandra is in the supermarket and queuing for some cheeses at the deli counter. The man behind the counter serves the lady behind her; she impatiently waits and then gets served afterwards. She carries on with the rest of her shopping, loads the car and feels stressed driving home, as she eats a couple of cakes out of the shopping bag. 'Stressed' – what is actually happening is that her subconscious is having an emotional dialogue going on which, if you could hear it, would sound something like this:

> *The man in authority behind the supermarket counter has just ignored me –*
> *I'm not worth it. Where have I felt this before? My father, who was in a position of authority, abandoned me because I reckoned he didn't love me or he wouldn't have divorced my mother. That was such a painful feeling (not feeling worth it) I don't want to experience that rejection again.*

As a result Sandra doesn't speak up for herself (as she is not worth it) and the 'stress' is all those remembered emotions of rejection and worthlessness which need temporarily suppressing with cake.

The hurt / happiness continuum is the same with the chemical reactions in the body. The sympathetic nervous system (SNS) turns on the fight or flight response. In contrast, the parasympathetic nervous system (PNS) promotes the relaxation response. And depending on the emotions, all manner of different hormones can be released into the body. Hormones are the chemical messengers produced by endocrine glands. Named after a Greek word meaning 'to set in motion', these hormones travel through the bloodstream to accelerate or suppress metabolic functions. I won't list all the different types of hormones and chemicals; suffice it to say there are limitless connotations of the effects of different quantities and mixtures of these hormones.

What I have seen through intuitive counselling and my *The Weigh Forward* programme is that destructive emotions create more destructive 'chemotional cocktails' which in turn may affect everything from liver function, appetite regulation, digestion and gastric efficiency.

## Exercise

Monitor exactly what you eat and drink over the next seven days – this is not a judgement on the types of food you eat and also must include everything which passes your lips, even if you don't class it as a meal or even a snack. Write down exactly what you were feeling and thinking in the 30 minutes before you ate or drank each time. Remember this is an emotional investigation and you are building the picture of what food you eat *with what emotions are releasing certain chemicals*. Try and avoid certain broad statements like 'I was bored'. Be specific: 'I was bored because I was on my own and felt I was waiting for my girlfriend to finish work so we could go and do something'; or 'I was unhappy because I had just come off the telephone with my mother who was having a dig about my crappy job again'.

| FOOD / DRINK | EMOTION | UNDERSTOOD REASON |
|---|---|---|
|  |  |  |
|  |  |  |
|  |  |  |
|  |  |  |
|  |  |  |
|  |  |  |
|  |  |  |

# 6

## THE CONNECTIONS BETWEEN WEIGHT AND ILLNESS

*The Weigh Forward* has so far helped us recognise deep-rooted patterning as a result of emotional events. This cellular disease within the body can manifest, as do other inter-related health issues. The medical profession will often talk about 'stress' and the 'power of the mind' in healing but current medical practices are – whether we like it or not – surgery and pharmacologically centred.

At some stage a willingness to recognise how powerful our subconscious thoughts and emotions are has to be taken on board to enable ownership of our body's health and wellbeing. If there is an ongoing suppression of emotions and cyclical negative and destructive thoughts, this disharmony within our body will often manifest itself in some way or other.

There are marvels and also failures of science and medicine, and it's similar for holistic practices as well. It wasn't so long ago that doctors drained blood, cut out parts of the brain and administered all manner of 'cures' in good faith, only for time and history to make a mockery of previously accepted practice.

It is the intention of *The Weigh Forward* to broaden your belief systems and challenge what accepted beliefs you have around healing and the power of your own body to heal when thoughts and emotions are in positive balance.

For example, Phillip weighed 30 stone and had spent years on a merry-go-round of street psychologists, six-month stints in famous rehab clinics and all manner of 'physical' approaches to his weight. When he embarked on his *The Weigh Forward* programme, not only did he lose a substantial amount of weight, but his acute psoriasis cleared up too. He had tried every pharmaceutical product for psoriasis over a ten-year period to no avail.

On an emotional level, psoriasis is rooted in deep-seated father rage and is an outward expulsion of that rage from the liver (95 per cent of all skin conditions in my investigative experience are caused by a sluggish liver). The liver is the organ of the body that suppressed anger has the greatest effect on. Remember the liver is the 'master' in terms of bodily workings, performing over 500 functions including:

- Processing digested food from the intestine.
- Controlling levels of fats, amino acids and glucose in the blood.
- Combating infections in the body.
- Clearing the blood of particles and infections including bacteria.
- Neutralising and destroying drugs and toxins.
- Manufacturing bile.
- Storing iron, vitamins and other essential chemicals.
- Breaking down food and turning it into energy.
- Manufacturing, breaking down and regulating numerous hormones including sex hormones.

- Making enzymes and proteins which are responsible for most chemical reactions in the body; for example, those involved in blood clotting and repair of damaged tissues.

The previous chapter on 'Chemotional Cocktails' highlighted the chemical and hormonal responses to emotions and even the term 'bilious', applied to angry people or thoughts, is derived from forgotten knowledge of the emotional link with the liver and anger / rage.

Once Phillip cleared his deep-rooted anger at his father (his psoriasis started the day his dad died) his skin condition cleared up and ever since he has been able to manage the onset of skin irritation by recognising how male anger has surfaced in his everyday life. With Phillip, his father had always said he would never be good enough and a whole host of other destructive comments about his son's life. Subconsciously Phillip felt 'I'll show him' so when his dad died, unconsciously, his body reacted by knowing he could never show him. So it 'spewed' the suppressed anger out into his skin. Every time Phillip experienced thoughts of not being good enough, the psoriasis flared up.

What has become clear to me over the years is that the specific weight related illnesses and their chemical make-up are also linked to certain foods and a return to what I have termed 'Chemotional Cocktails'. Similarly to the liver and its response to sugars and carbohydrates, Polycystic Ovary Syndrome (PCOS) is another weight related illness that has a chemical association with addiction to carbohydrates and sugars and is primarily driven by the profound ability of these foods to stimulate our neuro-chemical pathways – the brain circuits that produce feelings of contentment and dull emotional and physical pain.

The circuits stimulated by high carbohydrate foods and sugars are the same addictive circuits that are stimulated by drugs such as alcohol, cocaine and heroin. This is why I recognise that dieting is so difficult – and willpower is not enough – to make a permanent lifestyle change.

Exercise is one way to stimulate many of the same circuits, as are drugs and certain high carbo-hydrate foods and sugars (primarily dopamine, endorphins and serotonin circuits). However, subconscious emotional healing and re-patterning is the key to positively attuning these critical pathways, in order to ultimately lead to pleasure and emotional balance.

PCOS is one of the most common endocrine (or hormonal) disorders and is characterised by multiple abnormal cysts in the ovaries. Researchers have also found a link between Polycystic Ovary Syndrome and other metabolic conditions such as high levels of obesity, LDL (the 'bad' cholesterol) and high blood pressure. Because insulin production of the pancreas is thrown off by its resistance, the conversion of food to energy is impaired and there is an increase in the amount of stored fats. When glucose cannot enter the cells efficiently, it remains in the blood stream, causing elevated blood sugar which is sent to the liver. There it converts to fat and is stored throughout the body. When the body takes in calories, it has a choice of either burning those calories for energy, or converting them to fat and storing them. In patients with Poly-cystic Ovary Syndrome, insulin resistance encourages the storage of fat and the production of excessive amounts of the male hormone, testosterone.

What is vital to recognise during your process of healing with *The Weigh Forward* is that these chemical reactions are exacerbated, if not fully controlled, by the subconscious to ulti-mately create the chemical environment of 'protecting' you with the cushion of weight. To use the example of PCOS, its emotional cause, in my understanding, is where there has been either strong abuse by a male in childhood or severe emotional 'stunting' because of a controlling fa-ther. It results in hardened thought forms about femininity and female sexuality, and with the ovaries being the 'points of creation' symbolically to the subconscious and also the creation of children, the body stores the cellular memory in this area; subconsciously attacking your own femininity to suppress the vulnerability of past hurts and also, on an even deeper level, making pregnancy more difficult so your child doesn't have to 'suffer' like you did.

Pregnancy is also a major issue tied in with weight because of this subconscious association of trying to protect you from having to re-live certain childhood hurts and vulnerabilities that you suffered while your child progresses through the same stages. PCOS also results in the body creating an insulin resistance so it can layer more protection of fat and also increase testosterone. The feminine is less vulnerable to 'male control', an 'if you can't beat them join them' subconscious attitude.

For example, Jodie was highly controlled by her father, whereas her brother (a year younger) seemed to have much more freedom. The control by her dad centred on her femininity – what she was wearing, her make-up, which boy she was interested in, having to be accountable at all times for her whereabouts and lots more besides. Her subconscious transmuted the anger at being female and the limitation she felt because of men into manifesting into PCOS. When healing her emotional subconscious, Jodie recognised that when the PCOS was at its worst – in her twenties – she was in an abusive relationship with a controlling boyfriend and addicted to carbohydrates and sugars. She did everything to dampen down her femininity and sexuality.

## Exercise

Answer the following questions:

- Using *The Weigh Forward* 'timeline template', chart every illness and period of ill health in your life so far.
- With your timeline, investigate what was occurring in your life emotionally – specifically in your relationships, and circumstances.
- If you have recurring bouts of ill health (metabolic illness / cystitis / thrush / vaginitis / eczema / psoriasis etc.), again chart exactly when you first suffered the illness and the subsequent times and make the emotional connections.

- Complete *The Weigh Forward* 'Guided Visualisation' on emotional clearing of core illnesses.
- Make a list of the trigger foods, or foods that you are more drawn to, during such illnesses.
- Investigate the key times in your life when you could fully embrace your femininity and sexuality (masculinity and sexuality for men) and when you 'dampened' down those aspects of your life. Make the connections to your relationships, controlling factors and the limitations you felt at those times.

### CORE ILLNESS VISUALISATION.

To access your visualisation visit www.theweighforward.com/visualisations or enrich your experience by downloading the app at the iTunes store from the link available from this same web page.

Finally, make sure that once you have read the chapter on affirmations and nurturing your organs from the inside out you apply the cleansing that feels appropriate to you.

# 7
## TRIGGER FOODS

You should by now be starting to build a picture of how your emotions will relate to your internal processes and also how the external aspects of your food and weight are beginning to become obvious. Following on from the associations to different parts of the body and the 'Chemotional Cocktails', the subconscious also associates certain food groups to help suppress different emotions.

In Claire's example, she was drawn more to dairy foods when she went to university. Milk is representative of mother's milk from a subconscious viewpoint and Claire craved milk and foods containing milk. Chocolate and cheese replaced Claire's lack of physical mothering.

Bread is another strong trigger food. Like milk, it is a staple that is easily accessible and has been part of our food for thousands of years. It sustains and fills us up – not to mention the religious connotation of the 'Bread of Life'. Some clients who are dealing with a subconscious belief of being unworthy in the eyes of God react poorly to bread because they feel undeserving. Because of this, the subconscious may associate it to bed-down and therefore may be drawn to bread to suppress feelings of emptiness or loss, using it as a 'filler' to quash these negative emotions.

Slice of Self-Punishment     Pint of Mother Issues     Suppressed Anger Flavour

There are two types of associations with trigger foods:

1.  The actual type of food such as dairy / bread / crisps / sweets / cakes and pastries.
2.  The event or timings that trigger foods: eating out in a restaurant; going on a journey and stopping off at a petrol station; celebrating someone's birthday with a cake; doughnut Fridays at work; nights on your own and ordering in a takeaway; or the food you eat, or don't eat, when you are shopping just for yourself (especially clothes).

## Exercise
Make a list of your main trigger foods. Again, be specific. If it's dairy, is it cheese, milk puddings or chocolate? If it's bread, is it toast, sandwiches or just bread and butter?

Also, make a note of what type of circumstances you associate with trigger foods (this may overlap with the timings in Chapter 2, but list them once again).

Below are some examples from my own clients:

- I always eat pizza when my boyfriend comes around, but it is punishment because I feel guilty sexually.
- I always get nervous when I have to travel away from home (scared something is going to happen when I am not there) and always stop at a garage and buy 'pick and mix' sweets which I never usually eat.
- Whenever my husband makes me feel bad about myself I put some toast on and can eat up to eight slices in one session.
- I remember everyone's birthday in the office as it is a great excuse to get a cake.
- It is always sweet stuff when I am on my own, or feel isolated and lonely (sugar can be the subconscious's way of bringing some sweetness into the day if someone feels jaded and joyless).
- I always eat crisps if I feel angry. It's almost as if I have to crunch something to compensate for that anger.

It is important to remember it is not necessary the food that is being eaten but the emotion attached to it. In most of these examples the trigger food is being used to suppress the subconscious emotions.

| TRIGGER FOODS | TRIGGER SITUATIONS |
|---|---|
| | |
| | |
| | |
| | |
| | |
| | |
| | |
| | |
| | |
| | |
| | |
| | |
| | |
| | |
| | |
| | |
| | |
| | |
| | |
| | |

# 8

## MIRRORS: WHAT OTHERS ARE REFLECTING IN YOU

Following on from understanding how our food and eating habits can reflect what is going on internally with our subconscious, if we then take the concept of mirrors further by looking at the people, the situations and the environment around us, it is incredible to discover how our external world and internal emotions are all reflecting our struggles with weight and body shape issues.

When I talk about 'mirrors' I mean that it's important to look at your close circle of friends, family and peers and see what they reflect in you in terms of their relationship with your weight. It could be some obvious examples: how many of the women you know, who struggle with their weight, have 'controlling' partners? It could be subtler. Were you to delve deeper, do you think of the slim members of your circle as 'mean spirited, selfish or unloved'? This is not a new concept for those of you who are interested in spiritual concepts and understanding, but can be very informative if you use the 'mirrors' around you to understand what beliefs or judgements with food and weight are being reflected back at you, or that you are absorbing.

For example, Sarah's mum, aunt and best friend were fat but very loving, giving, happy and non-judgemental people. When she was ten, her dad re-married. Sarah's new stepmother and stepsister were 'skinny bitches' and targets, and blamed for taking away her father's love. It created a subconscious belief that being slim was destructive. As an adult, Sarah's female boss and boyfriend's mother were slim, mean-spirited and selfish; her subconscious re-affirmed her

65

association of being slim with negative people. Subconsciously the last thing Sarah wanted to become was slim and, by default, mean, selfish and bitchy.

The subconscious, though, as I have explained many times already in this book, is very deep and clever in the way it can make associations and set up patterns of trying to protect you from pain. It is also a repetitive animal in that the more you tell it something (visually, through thoughts, by hearing something or continually experiencing something) the more it absorbs. So it may just be a case of you being overweight, surrounding yourself with an overweight circle of friends and the subconscious repetitively reaffirming that this is normal.

To leave no stone unturned, we now need to work outwards from your immediate family all the way through to the media you interact with.

## Exercise

In your Journal draw a web diagram similar to the one below, with you in the middle and fill in the names of your family, friends and peers who are also overweight. I then want you to summarise the traits of those people. Describe how you see them. What sort of people are they? How successful are they, and how do you think other people think of them as a person? This is not just about their weight. It is about their personality and how you would place them in your world.

1. Repeat the same for a diagram which includes all the main people in your life (family, friends, work colleagues, neighbours etc.), whether they are fat or slim and analyse the same traits in them as in exercise 1.
2. Repeat again for the celebrities you are drawn to or follow on television, as well as favourite characters in books or in magazines.

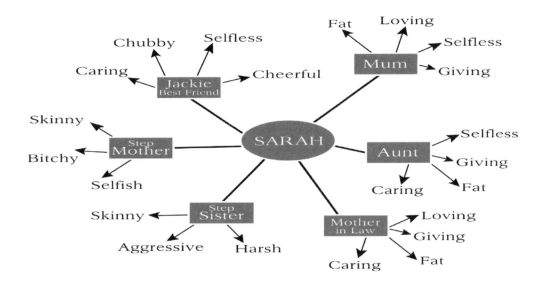

Finally, make a note of your day-to-day environment: where you live, where you eat, what bars, restaurants and cafés you go to, and see if they are mirroring certain beliefs you may have about food, weight and circumstance. An obvious example is the organic health kick (almost addiction) of Californian beach life, compared to the cheap greasy spoon cafés and chip shops of an English seaside town. (I am not drawing an economic comparison here, although if your investigation turns out to be based on fiscal beliefs driven by the 'cost' of anything 'nourishing' then expand on how you value food – what you feel about the cost of food, whether or not you feel money limits your relationship with food etc.)

# 9

## THE LANGUAGE OF WEIGHT LOSS:
## THE POWER OF YOUR WORDS

We are leaving no stone unturned in understanding our full connections to the outside world around us, and the full scope of our subconscious associations. It is important to recognise the power of our thoughts as the words and language we use carry feelings and beliefs that our subconscious will react to – *independently of our conscious mind.*

Remember, your own exposure to certain words by your parents, family and friends and the media and books you choose to involve yourself with creates your own understanding and patterning to those words – whether you speak them out loud, hear someone else say them or they are silent wordings in your mind.

Let's start literally with the term 'weight loss'. Weight, defined by our friends at Oxford, means to 'impede ourselves or burden with load; the downward force of a relative mass'. We certainly impede ourselves and burden ourselves with load when we are overweight, highlighting why weight is a result of emotional issues rather than merely an easily quantifiable physical equation.

I have worked with many clients whose strong subconscious fear of death has created a weight problem. Lucy had a strict religious upbringing in a cult and so much of her formative years were spent hearing of the 'retribution' that would be visited on her after her death, if she was a 'bad' girl. Her subconscious thought if she were physically impeded and slow on her feet, it would hold her back from walking (moving forward) to death and punishment from God. Every time she experienced life changes, such as moving house, changing job or even going on holiday, her weight increased dramatically. Her subconscious associated these changes with her moving forward – towards death. She particularly held weight around her hips, thighs and bottom, as if she were literally being held back and anchored. This contradicts all conscious thoughts and yet the subconscious contains a whole different world of understanding.

The word 'loss' in weight loss helps us understand this further – defined by the Oxford English Dictionary as 'detriment, disadvantage resulting from loss'. If someone has suffered the 'loss' (death) of a loved one at an early age, the fear of death and the pain of losing loved ones creates a strong fear within the subconscious. They may manifest behaviours such as finding it hard to throw anything away or crying uncontrollably at misplacing seemingly inconsequential belongings – all of which is seen by the subconscious as 'loss'. The last thing a person wants (subconsciously) is to lose anything – including weight! Maybe the weight loss industry should re-brand as Weight Release, 'release' defined as 'set free, liberate, to allow to move from a fixed position' – a word which carries much more positive emotion/reaction within the subconscious. To the subconscious, which has logged every single thought, emotion, experience, belief, observation, reaction or comment, the word 'fat' literally carries the weight of huge connotations, depending on the individual's pathway and its route to date with using that word.

Apart from obviously being defined as 'having excess flesh on the body', there are many sayings, including the following examples from clients I have worked with. Here, I have cleared old subconscious patterning where fat is seen by the subconscious as synonymous with success, opulence or abundance.

- Fat cat – rich, abundant, wealthy
- Fat of the land – fertile, rich, yielding, abundant
- Living off the fat of the land – best of everything
- The fatted calf – the best quality
- A bit of fat – good piece of luck

Conversely, negative subconscious associations with being slim can also explain why someone cannot lose weight. Beliefs about suffering, poverty, not being the best, infertility and so forth can be perceived as experiences of hardship which the subconscious does not want to revisit by being slim.

- Slim pickings – lacking, sparse, few juicy bits
- Slim chance of success – almost certain to fail
- Slim – small, insufficient
- Thin on the ground – lacking, few
- Thin – sparse or meagre, of low density, poor or unconvincing
- Thin blood/voice/humour/eloquence – weak, lacking an
- important ingredient
- Thin disguise/excuse – shallow, transparent, flimsy
- Thin-skinned – sensitive to criticism
- On thin ice – being in danger

There are also all the words that work in association with food, and with eating too. I have deliberately used terms like feed, digest or regurgitate (and others) when writing this book to show them in a different context. There are words like nourish, starve and

mercy Savin... on high note

victories

delighted

Cozy

hardiness

Strong

finish

opens

possibilitie...

pride

faith

compassionate

SKINNY

FAT

Health & Fitness

PROGRESS

believe

Great expectati...

great hair day

FREE OFFERS incentive

Freed: Families overjoyed at rele...

Show of support

Something to warm the heart...

on th...

Distinguished

Clear, calm message

live like kings

can't hurt us

Prospect...

tribute

TRIE...

LOOKIN...

DIET

Educat...

CLASSI...

dedicat...

Favora...

Joy

worst may b...

To th...

nefits

clean

Economy could

be...

Gold s...

of a comeback

content

WEIGHT LOSS

Portfolio

treats art

tasty

Squeaky clean

lovin' it

Takin...

SLIM

a dazzling p...

A bright idea

sweet

OK

wishes

happy

More good

news in

economy

THIN

PERFECT...

Opportunity award

Ready to get busy

Excellence

friendship

perfect

Christmas

perfect

A gift

health

No harm, no f...

rewards for m...

LIFE

50% OFF

a healthy fam...

safe

Earthly rewar...

Investments

success

empty, for example, which can emotionally mean many things to our subconscious.

I used the example earlier from one of my clients using the word starving. Remember, you have been bombarded by imagery all your life as to what starving means (Live Aid anyone?) and for the subconscious there is a deep-seated response about grasping hold of whatever is eaten – and overeating too – so not only would you eat more, your subconscious would create the chemical environment to store as much fat as possible to protect you from starving again. Other associated words, such as famished or saying how much you could eat, have the same effect. To continue in the same vein, diet contains the word 'die' and, interestingly, the word fatalism – containing the word 'fat' – means a belief that people are powerless to change their destinies.

As self-worth is our biggest challenge, it's imperative that we believe we are responsible for our own destinies and our thoughts create our reality.

## Exercise

Make a list of the words you use around food and eating, and also make a list of the words you use to describe your weight and your shape. Describe how you imagine your subconscious may be responding negatively to such words.

| WORDS USED FOR FOOD AND EATING | NEGATIVE RESPONSES |
|---|---|
| | |
| | |
| | |
| | |
| | |

| WORDS USED TO DESCRIBE MY WEIGHT/ SHAPE | NEGATIVE RESPONSES |
|---|---|
|  |  |
|  |  |
|  |  |
|  |  |
|  |  |

## Exercise

Now replace the negative words with less emotionally charged and positive words. As I explained in Chapter 1, the greater the emotion or the more intense the feeling behind words, the more the response from the subconscious.

*The body has to react to what you are thinking, so if you give it emotionally charged and vivid thoughts about yourself or your dietary habits it will start to create that reality for you.*

In my workshops many of my clients laugh at this initially and sometimes take it too literally. They might say, 'I know I say my belly is like a tractor tyre but it's not actually going to look like one.' And yes, it may not look like an exact Michelin replica but you will find your body responding by carrying weight fully around your waist, your actions of feeling the squidgy fat around yourself and the body even simulating the heavy hula-hoop feeling of carrying weight in that area. There is literally 'weight' behind what you say, and so to be able to speak out loud and also silently in positive, slim, fit and healthy terms will have a big difference on the physical manifestation of those thoughts. Self-effacing humour about you being fat or big, or whatever, is only destructive. *Master your thoughts and emotions and you will master your reality.*

I state the importance of mastering your emotions because many hypnotherapists and NLP practitioners concentrate on your positivity, but fail to emphasise how it is the silent sneaky thoughts that slip into your mind after trying to say positive statements that are more emotionally charged and shape your reality. It isn't about saying, 'Yes I'm great. I'm fit and slim and beautiful.' It is all about being able to say similar positive things and truly feel how important it is for you to take it easy on yourself – *to believe that you deserve to say such things about yourself.*

I will cover the structure of how you can say positive statements more in the chapter on affirmations, but when you replace the words, or your standard sayings, with more positive ones think carefully of how the subconscious will hear what you are saying. And remember, *words carry imagery – so keep the pictures in your mind which accompany your statements just as positive.*

## Exercise

Do you also find yourself describing your day as 'wasn't up to much', or do you tell friends you are feeling down in the dumps, or overly use negative statements that roll off the tongue yet are heard and reacted to by the subconscious?

Having recognised the power of your language around food and eating, use this exercise to explore the power of words in your daily life which may be holding you back. Are there statements about yourself that you use often to describe your mood, your routines or your general feeling about yourself that could benefit from a positive vocabulary overhaul?

# THE LANGUAGE OF WEIGHT LOSS: THE POWER OF YOUR WORDS

| OLD NEGATIVE TERM | NEW POSITIVE TERM |
| --- | --- |
|  |  |
|  |  |
|  |  |
|  |  |
|  |  |
|  |  |
|  |  |
|  |  |
|  |  |
|  |  |
|  |  |
|  |  |
|  |  |
|  |  |
|  |  |
|  |  |
|  |  |
|  |  |
|  |  |
|  |  |

# 10
## MOTHERING AND THE CHILD FACTOR

This has a dramatic association with weight and emotion. For women (and men) it is one of the most significant emotional connections of their life. Here, every aspect of the associations with becoming a mother, or mothering, is relevant; pregnancy, a miscarriage, terminations, ghost pregnancies, fertility programmes, taking on stepchildren, the menopause and many other related experiences, with such emotional heft that weight and the use of food to suppress these associated emotions is widespread. There is also the more subtle subconscious needs of 'mothering' – through family, friends and peers needing to feel worthy, and all the while the weight is protecting that person from not feeling 'taken care of' themselves.

Many women will have experienced changes in weight to some degree after having children. There is the natural baby weight to shift as the body settles back down after such a traumatic strain. However, having a baby is one of the most emotional experiences a woman can go through and it can set off all sorts of triggers within the subconscious. For example, the mother may become overwhelmed with feelings of responsibility for another being, or the fear that such a helpless loved one may come to harm. Having a child may provoke the fear of becoming trapped in a loveless, housebound relationship such as your own mother may have experienced, or a mother may actually relive their own buried emotions from childhood, as their child reaches the same ages of particularly difficult events in the mother's past.

Jane put on three stone when her little girl reached her fourth birthday. Only by working with *The Weigh Forward* was she able to unearth her own sense of loss over the death of her beloved grandmother when she herself was four. The subconscious – with its love of patterns – had associated her four-year-old daughter with Jane's own emotions of loss at the parallel age. Without getting to the bottom of what was happening subconsciously, Jane would have said she was 'comfort eating' because, for some reason, she was stressed. By working with *The Weigh Forward* and clearing long-held emotions of loss, she no longer needed to suppress those feelings and hold on to weight.

Other examples of clients' subconscious triggers around mothering:

- Sasha put on two stone very soon after 'deciding' to become pregnant. She had had a termination twenty years previously and all the feelings of self-punishment and feeling not deserving to have a child resurfaced. By not having shared this experience with her husband, she suppressed the emotions and stored them as 'protective' fat.
- Sharon, having suffered three previous miscarriages, was so angry at God (she was a strict Catholic) she put on five stone after the third miscarriage in almost as many months.
- Debbie, when she fell pregnant, put on so much extra weight that even the doctors were concerned how above 'the norm of pregnancy weight' she was. By working with *The Weigh Forward*, Debbie cleared a root traumatic block where her mother had been physically beaten by her father, causing her to be born prematurely. The fear of the same thing happening to her caused a high suppression of emotion and protective layers of fat. On a conscious level there was no way her husband, who adored her, would act in that way, but subconsciously, just being pregnant was powerful enough to trigger and stimulate her own womb experience.

77

- Sarah had two girls and had always maintained a balanced weight. After the birth of her little boy, she ballooned by four stone. During a *The Weigh Forward* regression there was a past life where as soon as she had provided a male heir for her husband she was ostracised from the family, and died a lonely, poverty stricken death. This trigger can be common because of a past life or as a result of certain childhood experiences.

## Exercise: For Women

In your Journal, divide three pages into three different sections and explore:

1. Your own childhood, your experiences around pregnancy, having children and being around children, including any stepchildren.
2. Your own mother and grandmother's experiences, especially when they had you or any siblings. Your perception of your mother's and your grandmother's role in life and relationships with the men in theirs.
3. Your own experiences of being a mother, looking after and being mothering towards others. What you perceive your role to be by being a mother and what experiences you would expect from living the life of a mother.

## Exercise: For Men

If you have younger siblings, write down in your Journal how your relationship with your mother was during her pregnancy with them. How was she with you? Were you expected to help once they were born? Did you get neglected?

If you had sisters, did you miss out on close time with your mother when they went shopping, or to your auntie's or grandma's?

Did your wife / partner have children before you were married / together? If so, how have you felt at differing times about their relationship? If you have had a child or children with your partner, have you felt, at times, neglected or taken for granted or excluded from the mother–child bond?

# 11

## THE GOD ISSUE

Sooner or later, while dealing with their subconscious and emotionally destructive patterns, clients will flag up concerns which affect them in some way, and which I describe as 'The God Issue'. It is, like one of those loaded words or expressions discussed earlier, loaded with connotations, beliefs and experiences. It always triggers reactions in people, reactions that are very often highly charged. If you are working with *The Weigh Forward* there are two main areas on a spiritual level that have to be looked at, understood and reconciled in each individual to move on: *the soul, and our subconscious reactions to 'God'*.

With all this talk about God, it is important that I state I'm not religious. I am a spiritual person. I believe religion is the man-made politics of God, created to control people through fear and guilt by means of power. Spirituality is the *experience* of God.

If we digest this, the first thing to investigate is whether or not you believe or feel comfortable with the idea of a 'soul'. If not, I would try to find a way to clarify the possibility of certain unique characteristics, emotions, behaviours, interests and reactions which you experience as being coded in your DNA. Feelings that have been developed and passed down in your genes from your ancestors and, within that cellular memory, certain things laid dormant only to be reawakened in your life. Either way, it's important to respond with some form of answer that feels right to you. I won't disagree that, quite often, people slip such questioning under the carpet of their minds so as not to deal with it. It has to be addressed in some form because the second aspect to deal with here is what I referred to earlier as the 'religious patterning'.

Strong emotions of fear, rejection, worthlessness, guilt and anger do surface from a cellular memory of negative past lives (or ancestral DNA, if you prefer) and can have an effect in this one.

Here are some examples of past lives which I have cleared for people I have 'regressed', and that have involved anger and the feeling of being abandoned by what can be termed as 'God':

1. A strict monk's life where Paul dutifully lived his life for God, and then the monastery was invaded and the monks killed. His soul felt abandoned by God as he had devoted his life to Him, and he hadn't saved the monks from suffering and death.

2. A 'witch' life where Josie had been a herbalist and seer in the village, helping others get better by using her connection to God. Then a villager dies and Josie is blamed, branded a witch and stoned to death – the soul again felt abandoned by God.

3. A nun's life where Sandra had an affair with one of the monks in the nearby monastery and got found out, to be ostracised from the convent and told to leave, where, without family and in a harsh environment, she died. Sandra's soul felt there was nothing wrong with being in love and yet was punished for it, even though her beliefs in God were of love.

As with all the above examples, they aren't the reality of any kind of God abandonment, but a consequence of how the soul judged the experience, imagining the abandonment and creating a cellular block to store in the subconscious. It is to be reawakened in another life

when triggered (or to follow in the beliefs of your great-great-great-grandmother, as all of your past is in your genes, if you prefer a more practical belief system).

I used these examples because, with those clients, their issue in this life centred around weight, when the blocked soul emotions from the past life was triggered and surfaced.

1.  In this life Paul, who had felt abandoned by God, found himself putting on weight when he started searching spiritually and he would also put on weight whenever there was conflict around him with family or at work – or even sensationalised in the news. To his subconscious, by searching spiritually, it was protectinghim by gaining weight and suppressing the fearful emotions because of the conflict. It would be deemed a highly irrational thought, but was very real emotionally to the subconscious.

2.  Josie, who trained as a reflexologist, and soon after started putting on weight, was still eating the same as she always had. When she was working in a bank, her subconscious felt safe because she wasn't 'healing' anyone. As soon as Josie started reflexology, her subconscious feared her not giving her clients the right treatment and, as a consequence, she would be severely punished (stoned to death). Her weight was protection from those fears and

the suppression of those emotions.

3.  Sandra, in this life, put on weight every time she was in a relationship and also tried irrationally to keep the relationship a secret. Her subconscious was responding to the fear that if her relationship was found out she would be punished and suffer just like her 'nun life'. The weight went on as suppression of the angry emotions, and the fear of being punished.

There are more connections and patterns with each of the examples above but I keep them succinct to demonstrate how 'The God Issue' can be triggered in the subconscious from something that consciously you would never be aware of. Having cleared many past lives for people and seeing the patterns emerge with clients dealing with weight or food/image issues, there are definitely certain themes that have been revealed.

1.  The soul feeling abandoned by God after having lived a religiously devoted life, and then suffering.
2.  The soul feeling angry at God for the loss, ill health, misfortune, poverty or poor decisions in their life because of their religious belief that 'it is God's will'.
3.  The soul being betrayed in some way and feeling there is no one to trust, especially God.

## Exercise: Spiritual Visualisation

Write in your Journal the answers to the following questions. You may feel comfortable only writing a few sentences, a few paragraphs or a few pages. There is no right or wrong way. Just be honest with what you feel.

1.  Do you believe in the soul? If so, what do you think your soul has learned and what is its purpose in this life? If you do not be-lieve in the soul, explain why, and then describe how coincidence, triggered emotions that make no sense and gut-feeling fit into your world, and how they are accounted for.
2.  Do you believe in a higher power? If so, what word do you feel comfortable describing this higher power as, and how do you picture it? If you don't, give a full explanation as to why you do not believe. (You need to exhaust your self-questioning here, including expressing any anger and sadness.)
3.  Are you religious? Do you follow a specific religion? Were your parents religious and if so how did that imprint on your upbringing?
4.  In difficult times have you ever said to yourself 'why me' or 'I don't deserve this' or 'if there is a God why would he allow this to happen?' If so, or you have said something similar, silently directed at God, or of feeling a victim, fully describe the situation which triggered you to say that to yourself, and what was going on emotionally at that time.

SPIRITUAL INVITATION VISUALISATION.

To access your visualisation visit www.theweighforward.com/visualisations or enrich your experience by downloading the app at the iTunes store from the link available from this same web page.

It is important to remember that any thoughts or emotions of blame or guilt prevent us from taking responsibility. Because of the very nature of religion being indelibly inked on our subconscious since pretty much the dawn of time, we have been strongly conditioned to live in fear and guilt because of an all powerful controlling *male* god that will judge, punish and visit retribution on our soul.

Depending on the religion, the misdemeanours may differ but will usually involve the 'usual suspects' of sex, sexuality, selfishness, greed, sin, impure thoughts, to name but a few.

This isn't a theological exposé or debate on the merits of religion. I'm trying to share an understanding that the subconscious mind is conditioned to put others' needs before its own. To very easily be triggered into fear of being rejected, thought of as not worthy, and being punished.

Whether we blame ourselves, blame others or blame God, we are only reiterating to the subconscious that we are victims, and worthless 'good-for-nothing' victims at that. And whether we feel guilty for what we have done, or for what we think we have done, to others, we again prevent the subconscious from knowing we can take responsibility and change or are just worthless idiots for allowing such situations to arise for ourselves or others.

# 12

## THE WEIGHT OF ABANDONMENT

We live in a world driven by fear and anger. Any newspaper on any given day is full of stories selling us emotions of fear and anger. Fear is provoked when we read about the latest terrorist act, murder, bacterial disease or rise in interest rates and our anger bubbles up when we read stories about our politicians' failings, parking or speeding fines, scams, unnecessary deaths; everything that is distressing to us.

Similarly, our own individual fears and anger go around and around, repeating and filling our minds daily, but don't allow us to get under the surface. If weight is the issue, the fears/angers of a holiday coming up and need to fit into a swimsuit/stick to a diet – even being worried about the new secretary your husband has hired – and a million other thoughts clutter our minds. *But the subconscious root issue of low-self esteem is buried underneath these distracting anxieties.*

I have already explained the real beliefs within the subconscious literally shaping our being and that the subconscious has been patterned to 'protect' you from these thoughts. Its need to hold onto weight makes you unable to shift the excess weight until the subconscious block has been recognised and released. Thoughts of abandonment will not be conscious, but driving the emotions and will be felt very powerfully, albeit without any understanding why.

The Abandonment Root Event will occur previously in your life and will either be the abandonment by a loved one, or an abandonment of the self. For example, Dad leaves home, or the child gets told she is useless and forsakes any belief in herself. Now we are getting to *Root Issues.*

Any form of abandonment will put someone into an imbalanced form of ego/responsibility, so the individual will either take over responsibility for everyone else, or feel unable to trust anybody and will only take responsibility for themselves. In both cases, there will be a deep core issue of having an aspect of low self-worth.

The subconscious will obviously be trying to prevent you from feeling that pain of abandonment again. It will take any vaguely similar situation and, in future times after the original abandonment you may do everything for another person (so they love you and don't abandon you). It may become highly controlling of situations and daily routine (so the rug isn't pulled from under your feet with a surprise abandonment) or become seemingly intellectual and non-emotional (don't care, then you won't be hurt by the abandonment); it might even make you become a rescuer / carer in your daily life and job (if I cure this alcoholic / drug addict / depressed person, I am curing my parent really and then they will love me). Whatever the situation of abandonment, the ultimate core-block and destuctive subconscious pattern is always *low self-worth*.

In all the abandonment examples given above, the subconscious thinks you have been abandoned because you weren't worth it. It was your fault. It was because of you. It wouldn't have happened if you hadn't been born. You could have prevented it if you had only been more aware or intelligent. You deserve it because you are useless. These statements may seem extreme, but that is how the subconscious has been patterned to react to abandonment.

When you are being asked to retrain your beliefs, how you think about yourself and how you feel about yourself, you can start to see why it is so, so important to begin right now taking it easy on yourself and replace negative thoughts and feelings with positive ones. (The chapter on affirmations will make more sense once you have digested this chapter.) However, positive thinking alone will never truly bring peace and balance to you without first recognising and then clearing the root events that triggered the destructive pattern within the subconscious.

Some examples of the root causes of abandonment – and consequently underlying low self-worth – are listed below:

## Root Causes of Abandonment

1. Being adopted
2. Being over four years older when a younger sibling is born
3. Father wanted a boy / girl instead of a boy / girl
4. Death of a sibling
5. Mother suffering – miscarriage / illness / depression
6. Physical abuse
7. Sexual abuse
8. Having to stay in hospital for any period of time as a child
9. Being a girl among many brothers or vice-versa
10. An alcoholic / drug dependant addict for a mother or father
11. A past life trigger of being 'abandoned by God'
12. An absent father / mother
13. A divorce and the father or mother leaves the family home
14. A strict / non-loving father or mother
15. A father or mother who travels or works away a lot
16. Losing a twin, either at birth or when a child
17. A death in the family of a 'favourite' (grandparent, aunt, parent, sibling) at an early age

## Exercise

Now you are ready to complete your main healing (clearing), complete the *core emotional block* visualisation.

### CORE EMOTIONAL BLOCK VISUALISATION.

To access your visualisation visit
www.theweighforward.com/visualisations or enrich
your experience by downloading the app at the iTunes
store from the link available from this same web page.

## Exercise

Answer the following questions in your Journal as a result of your visualisation and consequent
investigation.

1. My root event of abandonment was:

_____

_____

_____


2. I have punished myself in the following way on a subconscious level:

_____

_____

_____

3. My triggers in daily life as a result of my subconscious feelings of abandonment and low self-worth are:

_____

_____

_____

# 13

## 'FAT IS A FATHER ISSUE'

Susie Orbach labelled fat a 'feminist issue' and has offered many brilliant insights into the emotional links with gender issues. As a considerable nod to her work, I have found in working with clients, through my *The Weigh Forward* programme, that fat could also be coined as a 'Father Issue'. In understanding peoples' root emotional blocks of abandonment and self-worth, time and time again those who are at least three stone overweight all have suppressed emotional anger at their father or a father figure in their life (or even, as discussed earlier, at 'Father God' from a past life). It isn't too much of a leap to make for the subconscious – seeing that God has been referred to as the Father for thousands of years (and most people will have recited the Lord's Prayer at least once in their life). If I were a mathematician I would be exploring this problem:

FAT = FATHER ANGER SUPPRESSION AS A
RESULT OF FATHER ABANDONMENT

Interestingly, if it were a female client, I would probably put it like this:

## FAT = HER SUPPRESSION OF ANGER AT HER FATHER BECAUSE OF HIM ABANDONING HER

However, the wording isn't the point. In all my obese clients, the ones who have at least three stone of extra weight, the root event will always come back to a father-abandonment of sorts. Whether it's a full-blown abandonment by an abusive father, absent father or addicted father, or the more subtle rejection of a father by not expressing love, or showing favouritism to a sibling, it's always there. (Remember the list of abandonment in the previous chapter.) Whatever ways we have of justifying our childhood situation or experience, to our subconscious, the father is there to love us, to nurture us and to keep us safe and secure. Not only that, but the wide reaching use of the word 'father' shows with how many facets of our daily life that figure of authority is associated.

This should make more sense now, so let's expand on the sound-byte. Basically anyone who has suffered an abuse or a rejection from a father, a stepfather, someone acting in a fatherly role, or figure of authority, will have experienced a form of father abandonment. This includes actually becoming a father yourself (by marrying and becoming the man of the house or having a child) if you had a destructive relationship with your own father. (The subconscious in that instance will judge you then as your father, so the suppression of that anger turned in to self-loathing can be stored as protective fat.)

The important thing to recognise is that abandonment has meant a pattern of suppressed anger. (From when the abandonment was created the person would still hold out for the possibility of reversing it and gaining the craved love and approval.) Hence, to get angry and say what you were really feeling risks further rejection. The subconscious holds back such emotions, suppressing them with food and a protective cushion of fat. It also means that, as life progresses, the subconscious associates any male in authority, or one that you would desire love and approval from, as one and the same – your father. So, the suppression of anger and fear of rejection keeps happening, an exhausting destructive pattern, with all the associated reactions of food, overeating, holding on to weight and the fears, doubts, angers and frustrations that come with it.

# 14

## CHEMOTIONAL INTELLIGENCE AND HEALING

*Chemotional Intelligence* is merely the phrase that I have coined to expand on the chemotional cocktails from an earlier chapter. It is a good term, though, and more important than people realise. We are in a period of human consciousness when we have to understand our emotional responses to people and to the world, to understand why we act, feel and respond in certain ways, knowing that all those different emotions also release different chemical hormones.

The earlier chapters have talked about the subconscious and many of the patterns that can help you understand the bigger picture of your relationship with your thoughts and feelings/ food, weight, shape and body image. The key to making the most of this understanding is to clear and heal the emotional blocks that have been negatively affecting you.

If you have any negative preconceived ideas or feelings to the word 'healing' try and let them go, because to be able to re-pattern the subconscious we have to first be able to clear and 'heal' it; to use 'healing' in terms of a process to regain health – and we are overweight, continually stressing in our mind about food and body image, and contributing to our own ill health in this way.

There are many people who claim to heal on an emotional level, or by a clearing of negative cellular memory. I can only offer my own discernment of how I intuitively witness these processes. They are often vague in terms of not knowing exactly what the block is, and there is also the ego on the healer's part to take something away which your soul and your subconscious has chosen to experience and use as a lesson to learn from.

I find myself trying to be magnanimous to other healers and other processes, but the fact remains, just like any profession in the world, there are cowboys and charlatans. People who often haven't dealt with their own issues, opportunists, or people who treat healing others as a hobby or part-time vocation which makes them feel better about themselves.

The ability of someone to heal others is dependent on the work they have done on themselves. It is not necessarily the specific therapy, but more importantly the actual practitioner. I have seen a reflexologist re-route neural pathways to the brain to assist in nerve damage and I have seen another reflexologist glance at a chart, while working with a client, and say, 'It looks like your gut is a bit sluggish.' I have also seen kineseologists tap into a past life block and help a client release destructive cellular memory from that life, and have seen a different kineseologist do standard muscle testing and tell someone they are probably allergic to wheat.

The point of describing such therapies and practitioners is that the majority are limited in their abilities and understanding and, as a consequence, limit their ability to provide tools for deep clearing and healing. The old mindset of the healer taking away the discordance within the person, without that person being able to have full recognition of what set up that discordance – how that discordance has patterned their behaviour and experience – often means the tools to spend time re-patterning that programming will ultimately fail in the long run.

Remember every 'soul' chooses exactly how it will experience the lessons it has to learn, so that person has to be complicit and active in the full recognition, clearing, healing and re-patterning of their issues.

It is why many therapists have regular and dependant clients. The client experiences a temporary release and then the subconscious gets triggered and returns the discordance to that person. The therapist has triggered a unique need for themselves and what they see as their 'role'. (See my chapter about psychics with weight issues!)

To recap then, you are the perfect person to obviously investigate your own subconscious. All the visualisations and tools offered in this book are the most successful ways I have discovered to recognise, clear and heal emotional blocks held as cellular memory. As I said earlier, you have to fully embrace the work too as all I can offer are the tools, but you ultimately are choosing to work with your own subconscious to achieve healing with these powerful processes. Although we are working with your subconscious and your cellular memory, these are not hypnotherapy or mind programming (NLP) techniques. We don't want to override your subconscious or try and replace a more positive programming over the top of the negative programming. This is emotional and spiritual recognition, clearing, healing and then re-patterning.

I can't 'make you slim', to quote the claims of many hypnotherapists. It would be egoistic of me to claim to do so, and also no one's subconscious likes being made to do anything, unless there is a negative pattern of subservience. What I can do is offer very powerful knowledge and the tools for you to explore and instigate your own deep-seated healing to become slim – that is 'real' healing.

I often use the term 'cellular healing' with my clients and those who are comfortable with the levels I work on. The way we are advancing on a spiritual and chemotionally-intelligent level in understanding the 'soul' and the subconscious has come about by being able to understand the hidden influences of your DNA and, hence, your cellular patterning. The positive side of science and medical research (and yes, I feel there is a negative side to science and medicine too) is actually researching in this very area. However, there are always spiritual and intuitive understandings which are ahead of the game, and have already proved to have been so by pre-empting scientific discovery.

To recognise, clear and heal a cellular block can be undertaken in a few different ways. The accompanying visualisations with this book are a process where I guide you through the ways

I work, to take you on a journey to your subconscious and then work with the younger aspect of yourself which experienced the root event behind the destructive belief system. The process gives a chance for the younger aspect of you to have a voice to explain how it was feeling and its story of what events shaped your fears and froze them in cellular time, responding for the rest of your life up to this date, as a result of those destructive emotions. (That's why, at times of emotional stress, you could quite easily recognise your grown-up husband acting like a seven-year-old-boy – because, emotionally, he is!) This younger aspect of you then has the chance to actually see how much you have achieved since that frozen age.

You need to see that time; circumstances have changed and, more importantly, the freedom to take responsibility and make changes has occurred. With this recognition, there is then involved a spiritual stage to the healing where the younger aspect of 'you' works with your connection to the higher source and contracts with yourself to go into any healing process. The point of 'visualisation' is that 'you' can then 'tidy up' all the loose ends, to clear and heal the destructive cellular programme.

Another way I have worked with clients over the years, to facilitate the subconscious healing and change, is to use a creative outlet (writing, painting, music and so on) to work in a similar way. If we take writing as an example, there are obviously a million different ways your mind would associate the purpose and process of writing. To use this creative outlet there are specific guidelines I have found work the most efficiently. Something I channelled for one of my workshops, at the turn of the millennium:

*Remember we are ultimately born into creation, from the source of the Creator and are here to create positively in the world in some way to link us back to the Creator. To work creatively will resonate on many levels you won't consciously be fully aware of but will be opening a channel to other higher realms that are within you and that are around you. Being creative is creatively being.*

From the earlier chapters in this book you will by now understand that to change any destructive pattern in your life – like issues with food, weight and body image – you have to clear the emotional event, the pattern and the associations. Similarly, if you choose to work with your subconscious, you have to remember just that; you are working with your subconscious so if you are looking to draw up and release cellular memory, your conscious mind will not be much help and will, in all probability, look to sabotage your efforts.

So some of the usual methods you might employ, when writing something like thinking about it first, then stopping and starting after sentences when you get stuck about what to say, or editing the spelling and grammatical structure as you go, are obsolete for the type of writing exercise I have developed in this book.

## Emotional Release Pages
You can do 'Emotional Release Pages' as often as feels right for you. Some people really embrace them and do them daily for a couple of months and then sporadically, when stronger emotionally challenging situations surface. Other people try them and find excuses not to do them again. If that sounds like a loaded argument in favour of doing them regularly – it is! When surfacing those negative emotions stored from your past, painful experiences, there is our subconscious's trepidation at opening a door on something which it has tried so hard to lock away. This fear is natural, but unwarranted. To actually write and release past emotional

hurts and present counterfeit emotions that have been triggered is actually a relief, once they have been released onto the page.

Earlier chapters in this book will have hopefully trained you by now to know that the subconscious thinks it's protecting you by suppressing destructive emotions, so it does require a statement of intent from you to be firm in your commitment. You do need to follow through with 'doing' the pages and reassure yourself that you are safe and secure and now ready to release old hurts and punishments. Anytime you choose to do your 'Emotional Release Pages', the following steps will help make them the most healing and revealing possible:

1. Try not to think about what you are going to write about, or what you feel may surface beforehand. Just pick up the pen and start. You live so much of your time in your conscious, rational, analytical mind that, the quicker you start your free-flow writing and let it segue into 'stream of consciousness', the better.

2. Write for a minimum of three pages of A4 paper. This will ensure you push through the initial resistance and distractive ploys of the subconscious.

3. Keep that pen moving at all times! Do not let it stop ... even if you are scribbling inane dialogue with yourself. Keep writing. Actually write 'this is crap and why am I bothering when I could do with a cup of tea and a biscuit' if that's how you feel. Write it all down and keep returning to 'how' and 'what' you are feeling as you write.

4. Start with how you are feeling, then ask (in writing) of yourself if you have felt this before. Keep delving under the surface of the events that you write about until you can ask (in writing) of yourself: When was the root event? What age was I? How was 'little me' feeling? Then, like the process I guided you through on the visualisation exercise, you can understand the story and state on the

page the intent of reconciliation and healing in a similar way.

5.   By all means keep the pages safe if you want to, but ideally you can shred or burn them (safely) after you have written them. You have to feel safe to write exactly what you are feeling and the first thing that enters your mind simultaneously as you write it. To be so honest and forthright, you have to know that no one else will read your pages and that you yourself don't have to re-read them – they are a release, not really for keeps. If this exercise is to be truly effective, you are actually 'puking-up' suppressed trauma and emotion onto the page in order to try and get rid of it.

NB. Read the section on the importance of 'ceremony' (page 102) as well to understand further.

Some of my clients are artists who draw, sketch, paint or doodle and feel completely at home in those mediums, so if they follow the same rules for the writing, but use stream of consciousness imagery transferred onto the canvas, it is just as powerful. I have been lucky to have seen some 'full-on' paintings my clients have done over the years that have perfectly encapsulated an age of the original trauma, feelings and pain of that time, the understanding now and the healing. Remember, though, they perfectly encapsulated an age of the original trauma, feelings and pain of that time, the understanding now and the healing. Remember, though, they are a release – not a finished product for other people's consumption.

It is important to stress here that the subconscious will release comfortably what you are ready to let go of. Please don't worry or be hard on yourself if initial trials with the visualisation and the pages feel only partly reconciled or not fully healed. The idea is to keep working with those tools of release to reaffirm to your subconscious that you are now ready to let go of your past. If you keep setting aside time for the visualisations and emotional release pages, the full story will be revealed to you, cleared and healed.

On a final note, more recently clients have asked if typing the pages at a computer or on a mobile device or iPad work the same way. In a nutshell, no. There is a definite difference with your body's relationship with typing as opposed to the physical act of writing down. It has nothing to do with being old-fashioned and everything to do with connection to what you are doing. The act of holding a pen and writing is an extension of your body. It is a kinaesthetic thing where cellular movement in your arm can connect directly to each cell and, by extension, keep the link flowing from cellular memory along your arm and out through the movement of the nib and the ink onto the page. Typing sets a barrier up between you, and punching out the characters on a keyboard comes out uniformly on the screen.

There is also the whole group consciousness and associated beliefs already ingrained in our psyche that everything is accessible at the touch of the button, that information is instant and disposable and that information accessed through typing of an emotional nature – sex, dating, financial and so on – is similarly 'easy come, easy go'. No, the work in this book is from the inside out and physically writing your pages down, instead of typing them, speaks volumes on so many levels.

# 15

## THE IMPORTANCE OF CEREMONY

Ceremony is a wonderful and increasingly forgotten tool that can have a profound effect on the subconscious. When I use the word 'ceremony' I am referring to the creation of a symbolic event that adds weight to your intentions – not your body!

This is especially important for the subconscious because, believe it or not, we have been patterned for thousands of years to respond to ceremonies, rites and rituals. Most of our holidays and landmark dates of the calendar year are actually based on Pagan ritual. Most religions have always used ceremony for all manner of occasions and, if you research it, you would be amazed how much ritual is involved in the process of government, the monarchy, politics and many important organisations. Ceremony gives the individual ego permission to relax and take a back seat, allowing the subconscious to absorb the intent, the symbolism and the imagery.

> '*When humans participate in ceremony, they enter a sacred space. Everything outside of that space shrivels in importance. Time takes on a different dimension. Emotions flow more freely. The bodies of participants become filled with the energy of life, and this energy reaches out and blesses the creation around them. All is made new; everything becomes sacred.*'
>
> Sun Bear

The ceremonies I suggest in this book have been used with many, many clients with results that never cease to surprise me or bring a smile to my face. The beauty of following one by yourself, as with all the work in this book, is the individual positive responses people get because it is their own investigation and story that is unfolding.

## Ceremony 1

The first ceremony is to release all the negative connotations to dieting, weight, food, image and body shape issues.  Gather together any old books, magazines, photographs, any pages you have written about the negative hold of these topics, and any clothes that carry destructive emotional energy around these topics. Ideally, a good old-fashioned bonfire in the garden would be perfect, but these days may be impractical, unsafe or not possible.

Burning the material in an old metal dustbin safely and securely would also suffice. If a fire ceremony to destroy (and let go of) the past negative imagery of your struggle with weight, shape, food and image is not safe or possible, then sit quietly and rip and tear the material into rubbish sacks and take them to the nearest tip. As with writing, whether you choose to burn or to tear up the old paraphernalia, it is the physical act of ripping and tearing, burning or discarding, that is important. As you take part in the ritual, keep saying to yourself over and over in your mind:

> 'I release the old … I now make way for positive new experiences … I release
> the old … I now make way for positive new experiences … I release the old …
> I now make way for positive new experiences.'

## Ceremony 2

Once you have completed your core block visualisation and pieced together the destructive pattern that has been running in relationship to food and weight, you are ready for another powerful symbolic release for the subconscious.

Depending on the nature of your traumatic emotional event, and the triggers of the subsequent pattern, gather together any photographs, letters, printed out e-mails, text messages, clothes, bits and pieces and emotional release pages relevant to the pattern, and again follow the same release ritual as described in Ceremony 1.

1. If you have suffered father abandonment and consequently struggled having loving male relationships, gather all paraphernalia which you have kept associated with these relationships and times of pain.

2. If you were bullied at school and have subsequently felt victimised by so-called friends, family, work colleagues and neighbours, make your gathering of paraphernalia geared around those destructive memories.

3. If you were hospitalised as a child, or left alone in some way, and have subsequently experienced strong emotions when enduring periods of isolation as an adult, make your choice relevant to those times.

# 16

## THE WEIGHT OF RESPONSIBILITY: DEALING WITH EXCUSES AND THE BLAME CULTURE

Come on, own up! Every one of us has an array of excuses for why we can't lose weight.

This is because, when you're unaware of your subconscious relationship to weight and food, the conscious mind searches out 'rational' answers as to why you must hold on to weight. Now you have worked with your subconscious and you understand the real reasons, it is time to let go of the habitual excuses that over the years have rolled off the tongue. It is interesting identifying the type of excuse that we use, for example:

- 'I'm big boned'
- 'I have a slow metabolism'
- 'The work canteen doesn't stock healthy food'
- 'The kids want to eat burgers and chips'
- 'It's baby weight
- 'My husband likes me to eat a proper meal with him'
- 'Junk food is cheap'
- 'Big is beautiful' – if only you followed up your inner thoughts with the same statement!

Don't berate yourself for making 'excuses' because, as you now know, it's the subconscious that is controlling your weight and, as your conscious mind does not understand this, it reaches out for excuses that make sense.

> There are no real reasons why you can't lose weight – just 'irrational' subconscious associations that keep hold of it.

When the excuses stop making rational sense to us, we evolve into blame; our weight problem is somebody else's fault or something else's fault – 'Vastly overweight man sues Burger King'; 'If my wife didn't give me such big portions…'

Blame takes our power away. It stops us taking responsibility for our own issues and ourselves. Blame, like the guilt mentioned in an earlier chapter,  does just that. It stops us taking responsibility. It is difficult to take responsibility, though, if you don't know the 'hows' and 'whys'. Now you do, it is time to release all the old restricting thoughts before moving on to affirmations, which will help replace and re-pattern, once you have cleared the Root Emotional Block.

## Exercise
Write down in your Journal the old sayings, thoughts and statements. Then write alongside them your new positive statements.

| OLD NEGATIVE STATEMENTS | NEW POSITIVE STATEMENTS |
|---|---|
|  |  |
|  |  |
|  |  |
|  |  |
|  |  |
|  |  |
|  |  |
|  |  |
|  |  |
|  |  |
|  |  |
|  |  |
|  |  |
|  |  |
|  |  |
|  |  |
|  |  |
|  |  |
|  |  |
|  |  |
|  |  |

# 17

## REPATTERNING AND REPROGRAMMING

Once your subconscious reasons for holding on to weight have been recognised and cleared by working through *The Weigh Forward* visualisations, then one of the most powerful ways to re-pattern the subconscious is by working with affirmations and positive imagery.

To clarify, the subconscious is like a super-computer that downloads everything it sees, hears, feels, experiences and witnesses from the second we are born. Any struggle with weight is a result of 'rogue programming' running within our super-computer, controlling our weight and reactions to food in a destructive way. Once 'cleaned' – through using the techniques in this book – we need to give the super-computer a clear and positive 'new programme' for our weight/food relationship (by affirmation and positive imagery).

### Affirmations

An affirmation is a positive statement we recite to ourselves several times a day for a given period of time to 'write' and 'bed-in' our new positive programme. It 'tells' the subconscious the new pattern and gives it a clear and specific intent. For example: 'I now love, value and accept myself'; or, 'I am slim, fit, healthy and lean'.

We may at first feel a bit silly repeating these seemingly bizarre sentences to ourselves, yet if you delve a little deeper you realise that prayer itself is a form of affirmation. Scientists, always the last to catch up, are now proving that thoughts – and words – can be used to transform

109

our body shape. Bodybuilders doing high-tech physiological studies proved that lifting weights while concentrating on the muscle getting bigger, and stating a positive affirmation ('My tricep is growing bigger now'), yielded the largest increase in muscle mass.

Not only are affirmations a continual imprinting into the subconscious of positive health, they are also halting the use of the old sneaky negative thoughts that were previously seeping into the subconscious.

Before you started working with this book, your blocked subconscious emotions were triggered and the negative feelings and thoughts were also triggering the neural pathways in your mind which strengthened destructive reactions. Each time you catch your 'self' from fully thinking or visualising the negative responses, and replace them with your positive statements, you are weakening and eventually breaking the old neural links and displacing them with strong positive ones. It does take time, and I always say use humour to help yourself as you re-pattern.

We have all watched a friend try to stop swearing. They decide to do it, then a few minutes later they swear, before recognising they have done it. Gradually then, over time, they catch themselves earlier and earlier from blaspheming, until eventually, they are catching themselves in their mind and ultimately just don't even trigger the thought of the swear word.

I say 'use humour' because don't lose sight of the fact that the core re-patterning of your whole subconscious and 'soul' is into self-worth. If you start punishing yourself, or give yourself a hard time, it is just more negativity. Just have a cheeky smile to yourself if you realise you have been thinking negative thoughts about food and your body, and let them go and say your affirmations. You may not recognise until the next day; you may well recognise an hour later and will experience recognising just after you said or thought it – just smile and replace – if you tell the subconscious often enough it does go in.

Catch yourself from sending negative thoughts and words to your body like 'my bum looks big', 'I hate my belly', or 'I'm fat' (remember the chapter on words) and instead send positive thoughts and use positive affirmations. I have already broken down your affirmations into core ones, numbered 1, 2, 4 and 5 (3 will be your personal affirmation) and have included a list to choose your main personal affirmation from once you have completed your visualisation, investigations and know where your pattern has stemmed from.

Affirmations are very powerful, but again we may have a slightly disappo5inting or cautious reaction to saying them because of a previous experience. Remember, if you have just tried to be positive in the past and kept saying positive statements, if you haven't worked with your subconscious to clear the root trauma, that event is more powerful and has had way longer to bed itself in, so just positive thinking without emotional healing will be like constantly trying to put a lid on a bubbling-over saucepan. This is why many people who experience hypno-therapy regress again at some point in the future because the destructive emotional pattern resurfaces. If you say affirmations as a form of just positive thinking or as part of a hypnotic 'override' then there are two things to consider here; first, an underlying feeling of imperma-nence and, second, an esoteric principle is at work.

- The Temporary Factor: to only undertake using affirmations as a form of posi-tive thinking and recommendations from, for example, motivational gurus will end in sabotage. Obviously any positive energy is better than a negative en-ergy in every single situation. We are interested in achieving a healthy long-term balanced weight and relationship with food and body image. Because that is our goal, affirmations have to be specific to you and follow the clear-ing and healing of the emotional block and pattern. Otherwise it's exactly the same as having a slight leak seeping through your wall in heavy rain. If you papered over that damp patch with new wallpaper, however luxuriant and dry it looked, as soon as the rain (strong emotion) occurred it would seep back through.With *The Weigh Forward* you are tracing that leak all the way back through the wall, the insulation (the protective layer of fat) and back to the hole on the outside rendering (the initial traumatic event). Then you are drying that channel to the source point and re-rendering with the best external waterproof cement, replacing new stronger lightweight insulation (no need for obsolete heavy fat protection) and finally choosing the perfect wallpaper for you, which will stay dry and in place for as long as you choose to let it.

- The Esoteric Principle: I had a split reaction when the book, *The Secret*, hit the streets and dragged a level of spiritual awareness into the mainstream. Part of me was joyful and excited that more and more people were waking up to understanding more levels of their existence and the possibilities available to them. However, the other part of me was frustrated for all the people who latched onto 'manifestation' and 'ask and you shall receive' sound-bytes without understanding how the subconscious works. If you state your intent to the Universe of what you desire, your thoughts will definitely work with your connection to the higher source, and look to manifest those realities for you. However, for us to receive what we would choose to positively accept (I don't like the words 'want' or 'need') it means that our subconscious has to think we are worth it, to receive our wish fulfilment into our life.

What it does first is start clearing the way towards that acceptance by throwing to the surface the destructive blocks of rejections and worthlessness, so we can deal with them and, internally, at our very core, be able to value ourselves enough to manifest physically into our lives. What I see happening on an invisible level is that people's intentions start manifesting their dreams, then their subconscious throws out the invisible blocks and barriers to slow down and stop them physically manifesting. This is what I have termed the 'esoteric principle' in relation to people only doing affirmations before clearing their emotional blocks. So you can jump around as many times as you want singing 'I am happy and slim', but because of the emotional blocks, the subconscious will silently answer: 'No you aren't. You are unhappy and it's painful because the vulnerability you felt when your father left was like a hole in your heart. The fear that any man will do that to you again is exhausting, and you can't be healthy because you keep telling yourself silently how tired and fat you are.'

Eventually the affirmations will fizzle out because, for your subconscious to accept you are happy and slim, it has to make you confront why, up till now, you haven't been happy and slim. So, if you have 'tried' affirmations before, don't give yourself a hard time because the temporary factor, and / or the esoteric principle, will have sabotaged your efforts, or your enthusiasm will have waned.

## Maximising Your Affirmations

It's interesting that sometimes in my workshops, or even with a one-to-one, where, despite spending much time explaining the importance of affirmations and the 'hows' and 'whys', people will sabotage almost immediately. ('I lost the piece of paper I wrote them down on'; 'I changed it slightly to read better'; 'I spread them out over the day'; 'I do triple on Mondays as I usually miss the weekend' etc.)

Over the years, I have fine-tuned how clear I am when talking about affirmations knowing that, because they are the 'post-healing' facilitators of replacing the old negative conditioning with a new positive one, the subconscious will pull out all the stops to initially try and dig its heals in, to sabotage any change. This can include silent thoughts doubting the affirmations or their importance. It can subtly try and move the goal posts, through wording or the amount of times you say it, and also keep you busy and distracted by avoiding saying them. Anyone who has worked diligently with affirmations will easily identify with the types of sabotage already mentioned.

The first thing to do is never underestimate the importance of saying them. Remember, when you have cleared your core emotional block and recognised your destructive patterns around food, weight and body image then the affirmations will, over the next thirty days, filter the residual destructive patterning out of your cellular memory, your energy field and your daily experiences. To do this, it will challenge you with tests to see if you do really feel a truth to what you are saying, through your interactions with others and your own thoughts.

For example, if someone is saying the affirmation 'I have released all destructive emotions of self-punishment, and I love, value and approve of myself' then, especially over the next thirty-three days, small incidents similar to the past will crop up testing you to recognise that your husband losing his car keys, for example, is not actually your fault. (The silent thought of 'I'm a stupid idiot, I should have noticed where he put them', would be the old pattern of self-punishment.) To be able to recognise the uncomfortable feeling in your stomach, as he gets angry because he can't find the car keys, it needs to be recognised as his responsibility, as you affirm to yourself, over and over in your mind, your affirmation.

The above example is also very apt because it may involve your husband blaming you, or it may involve him unnecessarily shouting or making you feel uncomfortable and part of your 'action' would be to say, calmly and directly, that he has lost his keys, you will help him look for them, but he has no right to blame you or make you feel uncomfortable. This truth is releasing what would have remained as suppressed anger and also reiterates to the subconscious that you value yourself. To some, the example may seem obvious or flippant and some people would wonder what the fuss is about, but so many of my clients over the years have found themselves in an almost mirror image of that scenario. However, whatever the little tests that crop up in daily life involve, the sooner they are recognised as challenges to let go of the initial emotional response, and calm down with repetitive affirmation, the better.

## How To Say Affirmations

With affirmations we are ultimately telling the subconscious what it is going to accept – that's the bottom line: tell it enough times and it will sink in. Knowing this, though, you can see the continual battle that would spring up if the emotional block wasn't cleared first because, although you would be repetitively telling the subconscious the positive statement, you would also more powerfully (with emotion) be negatively affirming the destructive pattern.

Because you are dealing with the subconscious and the 'soul', probably the most powerful way to say your affirmations is to look yourself straight in the eye, in front of a mirror, and say them out loud to yourself. However, we are dealing with the subconscious and not the conscious mind, which would logically and rationally think 'well, if that's the best way, then that is the way to do it' – not necessarily!

Consider that it's like climbing a rock face; the ideal way to the top may actually present too many ways to become stuck, to slip, to fall or to fail, whereas another more gentle way will be more circuitous and take a little longer, be a bit repetitive but definitely see you to the top. That's what we want. To see you rise to the top.

I could 'go all philosophical' with the discussion at this point, and say it would be negative to think about the obstacles and possible failure, but the reality, with this book, is that you are just starting to find your way with your subconscious, and you are ultimately working on your core self-worth.

To pick the hard route could actually be your subconscious setting you up to fail, and then not have to change, because you fall back into self-punishment for not doing it.

The most important thing is that your affirmations get said and they get said at least *eleven* times a day, and for at least *thirty-three days in a row* (I'll explain the numbers later).

When I first started saying affirmations, I would record them and play them in the car and say them to myself in my head at the same time. Nowadays, with MP3 players and voice memos on telephones, if someone wants to record them and do them that way, it's easy. Part of recording and playing them is that you hear your voice out loud and with the privacy of headphones, if you wanted to, and you don't have to count eleven times. It's by no means the only way to do them, just an example of a way to make it easier. (I have hundreds of clients who say them in their mind and discreetly keep track of how many times with their fingers.)

## When To Say Affirmations

There are two main components as to when to say your affirmations; first, the timing for the main block and, second, the anchors throughout the day. Ideally, it is best to say your affirmations in the morning, as it will clear part of your energy, set you up for the day and give you greater opportunity to continually say them when you get triggered. The other thing is that if they are left until last thing at night before you go to sleep, when the subconscious is in testing mode, it will send you to sleep and miss the pattern. (I explained earlier that the subconscious is like a super-computer hard drive that has logged every single feeling, thought, experience, interactions, etc.)

Each morning, it's like a floppy disk is loaded and the whole day's feelings, thoughts, experiences and interactions are logged then (here is the important part) at night, when you go to sleep, that floppy disk is downloaded onto the hard drive of the subconscious. (One aspect of dreams is this sifting through and filing correctly what has been logged during the day.) More importantly, though, is if you go to sleep before having said your daily affirmations, there will be a glitch in the new positive programme you are writing into your subconscious. If it is for thirty-three days in a row, then you have to keep track somewhere, to literally tick off every day and start back at day one, if you miss a day.

I have said often in this book that the subconscious loves patterns, so it is preferable to try and get into a routine of when you say the main block of affirmations, and associate it with something you do every single day. An obvious example is a post-it note by the kettle with the word 'affirmations' to remind you at a time where you may every single day, like clockwork, go down into the kitchen first thing in the morning and put the kettle on – perfect time, perfect reminder. Some people have a note by the bathroom mirror, and do it while they are shaving; others as a bleep alert on their mobile phone. It makes no difference, as long as you stick to the routine daily.

For example, I was on day thirty-one once during a set of affirmations, and although I felt I wasn't going to be in the car the next day (Sunday), I didn't take my tape out on the night before and, of course, wasn't in the environment for the daily reminder and forgot. It is very easily done, so never underestimate doing them, and you will certainly have greater success.

When I talk of 'anchors', I mean being able to say your affirmations, or deriva-tives of your affirmations, when you get emotionally triggered during your daily life. It may be a specific person in a relationship that is your main challenge, turning up and pressing your buttons, or it may just be random thoughts sneaking out while you are doing something else. They are the moments when you have a perfect opportunity to nip the destructive emotion in the bud and 'anchor' the new pattern in. I explained earlier about changing the synapses in the brain that have previously linked certain situations, experiences or emotions (thoughts and feelings) to a destructive way of thinking. Each time you get triggered is exactly the time to halt the negative thoughts and feelings and replace with your affirmations.

Because the affirmations will have been imprinted from the day in the main block, you can say any of your affirmations or derivatives of that affirmation, thousands of times a day if you want. For example, your thoughts start wandering to your partner and how you im-agine she may be taking you for granted. You are able to halt that chain of thought and rea-

firm a part of the example affirmation above and keep repeating 'I value myself'. The clients who move on the quickest are the ones who embrace their affirmations and police their own thoughts and feelings throughout the day to halt and replace when they are 'triggered'.

## The Construction Of Affirmations

Many people have commented on affirmations over the years and there are different understandings for doing them. I can only share with you what I worked with and developed to maximise the effectiveness of them with my clients.

Remember, these affirmations are 'post-healing' affirmations for you and specific to you. Yes, even the group ones that I include are the deep, deep patterning of reminding the subconscious it is safe and secure and protected by your light at all times. That it is free to release certain destructive emotions and free to forgive yourself and value yourself. These ones are because I have delved into certain traits of root patterns within everyone's subconscious. Whatever your own individual emotional block is, it will have an abandonment theme and a low self-worth theme, with a disconnection of some sort from the source. These are core soul affirmations, the remainder you will choose depending on the nature of your clearing. With your affirmations, understanding that the subconscious doesn't register negative statementslike 'don't', 'not', 'never', 'won't', etc., it is ideal to keep the statement personal; for you to use the strength of the indent of 'I' and considering the subconscious not recognising a negative, to keep it positive.

When I tune into someone on an intuitive level it is fascinating to watch the subconscious completely skip over the negative command. It is a fact that the subconscious cannot recognise a negative. If your affirmations include statements like: 'I will never be overweight again'; 'I won't eat chocolate'; 'I am no longer fat'; then the subconscious will hear and act on: 'I will be overweight again'; 'I eat chocolate'; 'I am fat'. The subconscious acts on what it is told, but not if that includes a negative command or statement.

You have to really dissect what it is you are actually saying and how the subconscious is digesting it. As well as not recognising negative statements the subconscious will act literally on dubious words such as 'want' and 'need'. For example, if you state 'I want to be slimmer' or 'I want to reduce my body fat', the subconscious will create a 'want' ensuring that the 'want' remains in your intention, and the same goes for 'need'. It says to the subconscious that there is a need and goes about creating a reality of always 'needing'. This is why I keep affirmations in the present tense. If you state 'I will be slim next year', the subconscious will stick you in a continual cycle of aiming for next year, so will keep you on the 'never never' of a 'next year' which will always remain in the future. If you are specific and say, 'I will be slim for Christmas' then, lo and behold, you may be, but only at Christmas. I am not being pedan-tic, merely outlining how the subconscious operates. Also, there is the esoteric principle I explained earlier. If your statements are in the present, the subconscious has to go about clarifying that and drawing to the surface any residue that may be preventing that statement being a reality, which is why, if your affirmation is based in the future, that is where it will remain because it won't have to act on clarifying it in the here and now.

When I talked about 'self-worth', I mentioned how we are conditioned to put others' needs before our own. The qualities of being self-effacing, humble, and a host of other attributes that basically stem from conditioning of not wanting to be seen as selfish, cocky, arrogant or vain can be a real hindrance for you when doing affirmations. It is time to get over it and recognise that we are all too quick to give ourselves a hard time yet have all manner of excuses when it comes to saying positive things about ourselves. You are re-patterning your own subconscious. You are not having to scream from the public pulpit how amazing and wonderful you are (that's next week – just kidding), so you do have to get your head around the fact that, yes, you love yourself, and that, yes, you value yourself, and, yes, you approve of yourself, and, yes, you are free, and, yes, you are slim, fit, healthy and lean.

*The whole point is you may not feel instantly comfortable with certain statements but the subconscious has to be told in order to change.*

When I wrote about the power of thoughts earlier and that the negative thoughts that were powered by emotion were more powerful, it obviously works the other way too – the more you can say your affirmations with conviction, strength and passion, the more powerful they will be and the easier they will be received. So I suggest for once not eating your 'humble pie', and eating a 'good helping' of self-love instead.

## Numerology

Some of you may well be wondering why I have said specifically to complete your main block of affirmations, eleven per day for at least thirty-three days in a row.

First, for a new pattern to sink into the subconscious, it has to repetitively go in for a period of time. We can trace this back to ancient times and the full cycle of the moon or, more recently, many people aim to exhibit change after a month.

Numbers are, in a way, older than language. Our subconscious understands the deep resonance of numbers and if you work with numerology, as I do, you will see the power of certain numbers and the 'vibration' of those numbers with regards to daily life, your birthday dates, an athlete's shirt number, etc. I find it very interesting but, more importantly, I can intuitively see how the subconscious responds to numerology.

Anyway, with regards to how over the years I have structured affirmations, I work with what are called 'master building numbers'. In numerology, any combination of numbers will 'break down' into a single digit and although 11, 22 and 33 can become a 2, 4 and 6, they remain as 'master builders'. They are highly charged numbers and they possess more potential than all others, but they are also much more difficult to handle and they need time, maturity and effort

120

to integreate into one's personality. They are very challenging and also highly paradoxical; they promise enormous potential, but at the same time they can create lots of inner tension, coming from a deep desire to achieve something extraordinary. They are perfect for our use as affirmations for re-patterning, because having cleared the core emotional block you are more than ready to handle the inner tension of release as they embed positively into the subconscious.

Eleven is the most intuitive of all numbers. In numerology it represents illumination; a channel to the subconscious; insight without rational thought; and sensitivity. It is a number with inborn duality, which creates dynamism, inner conflict, and other catalysts with its mere presence. It is a number that, when not focused on some goal beyond itself, can be turned inward to create fears and phobias. Eleven walks the edge between greatness and self-destruction. Its potential for growth, stability, and personal power lies in its acceptance of intuitive understanding and of spiritual truths.

Indeed, eleven is attributed by many numerologists as able to bring peace not so much in logic, but through faith.

Thirty-three is the most influential of all numbers. It is the Master Teacher Thirty-three combines the numbers eleven and twenty-two and brings their potential to another level, which is exactly what we are all aiming for through achieving change by reading this book.

## Core Affirmations
1. I am safe, secure and protected by my light at all times.
2. I have released all destructuve emotions of fear and anger. I am now free to be me.
4. I love, value and approve of myself. I am loved, valued and approved of by others.
5. I am slim, fit, healthy and lean. I am beautiful.

## Personal Pick Affirmation

3. I have released all limiting beliefs (shame / guilt / hopelessness / powerlessness / worthlessness). I now embrace my positive strength, power and self-worth.

Depending on what you felt was the most powerful association with the choice of words above, after your clearing, insert that as the main word of your personal affirmation.

# 18

## DNA AND ENERGY VIBRATION

I've already touched on the realisation that our thoughts create our reality. It is also true, in my understanding, that we are all energy and vibrate to the tune of the energy of our environment and those around us – unless we are enlightened and able to work independently on our own connection to the source, and our own energy, clearing and resonating techniques.

Our DNA carries a complete reflection of who we are. It is moulded by our thought forms, mutated by our emotions and transformed by our toxic environments, diet and group consciousness belief systems.

Scientists have proved that there are other influences occurring within the tangible two-strand DNA witnessed under their microscopes – what I would call 'etheric influences'; in other words, the coding of everyone's 'soul' journey and its higher knowledge potential. By working on clearing blocked emotions and re-patterning old and negative thought forms, you are actually raising the vibration and possibilities of your DNA coding.

Here's an example. Those scientists' initial failures while cloning Dolly the Sheep were overcome by transmitting pulses of electricity and light through the strands of DNA. In essence, this is what we are doing when clearing our emotional blocks and destructive thought forms and belief systems. We are increasing the light and the vibration of the 'etheric' strands of DNA and literally becoming enlightened.

Scientists are witnessing the change in the DNA make-up of some children born now.

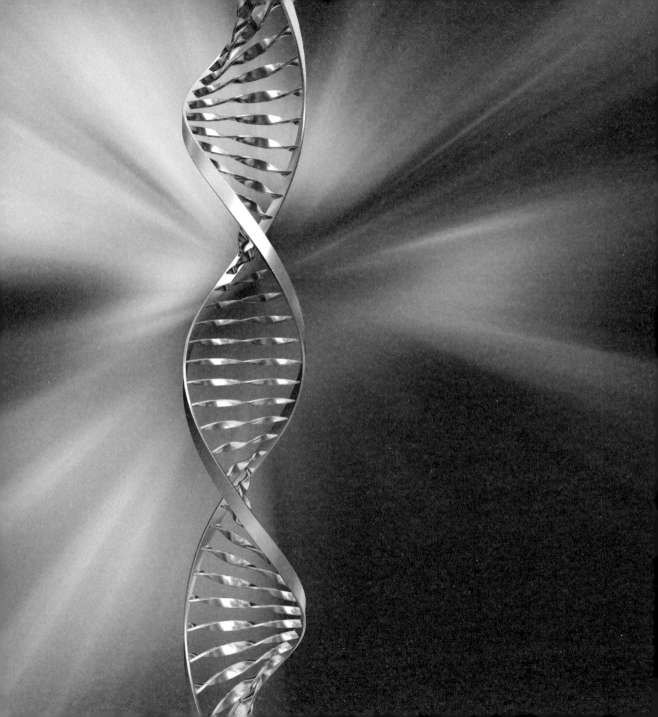

Whatever their explanation, it is an awakening of higher knowledge and wisdom that has been dormant in our generation's coding, keeping us stuck in illness, depression and limited or destructive thinking. By taking full responsibility for our soul's karmic choices, our choices of family, relationships, thoughts, beliefs and experiences, then we can own our choices, clear our emotional blocks and raise the vibration of our DNA.

This transmutation of your DNA is not only possible but occurring in every moment, determining which molecules, chemicals and hormones are being created within each cell through DNA transcription, linking you to vast and completely unlimited possibilities of health and physical creation. If that sounds like science fiction, New Age mumbo jumbo, or out of your grasp, it isn't. I have tempered my spiritual knowledge and understanding for the purposes of this book, but if you research any of the areas discussed on DNA you will find that both the scientific and spiritual communities are starting to realise the true potential of working with cellular memory and cellular patterning. During the writing of this section of the book, I have deliberated on how much or how little to share of my findings with relevance to my work with *The Weigh Forward*, and I feel it is better to include an overview of energy and provide a platform for you to investigate further, if you resonate with the information.

I set the scene with our very own DNA, to help understand the reality of matter and vibration. With my non-scientific tongue, I would state that we are all vibrating matter. Studied under the microscope, we are molecular, atomic and Quarky (yes we are quirky too, but I mean the elementary particle view of matter). As with DNA, scientists will differ in their definition of molecules, particles and matter. My understanding of what I see intuitively and have witnessed with clients, is that everything is basically vibrating matter – from ourselves, through the visible furniture in our house to the paper on our desk, to the invisible wind, oxygen and radio waves all around us.

All these different types of energy vibrate at different levels, but what is important for your investigation is that your environment will in some way resonate to the same tune as you. If your negative thoughts about your food, weight or shape are consuming you, the power of those negative thoughts will seep into the very walls of your house, begin to attract certain people around you that reflect that and keep you in a microcosm of the same vibrational belief system.

In simple terms, your grandmother lives in a house for thirty years and after she dies you can literally feel her presence there. I read a study last year which suggested scientists thought cancer could be viral, considering many couples contract the same type of cancer. I would offer the suggestion that it isn't viral, but vibrational, and if the negative and destructive emotional blocks, thought forms and belief systems are the same and you spend a lot of time with a person, the cells begin to vibrate to the same tune (a sympathetic string, if you will).

Returning to your own investigation of *The Weigh Forward* but on a much simpler note, many people who start to lose weight will notice that they are having big clear outs, moving furniture, changing uses of rooms in the house and also spending more or less time with different friends and members of the family. This is a perfect example of clearing and healing and hence vibrating at a different level to those around you. Something has to give, and if you are committed to healing yourself, it will be the people around you who related to an overweight 'rescuer' and did everything for everyone else because it benefitted their energy, which now has to move on and find someone else to fill that role.

The same process goes for why unconsciously you may be motivated to clear out the house, changing things around – basically shaking up the old, stagnating vibration of energy and giving it a chance to raise its level with your new aspirations.

## Exercise

The following exercises are not definitive. They are broad brushstrokes of the three areas to shake up around you for the Positive (higher vibrations): Home, People and Daily Habits. I list some examples below of what previous clients 'shook up' in their life after clearing their emotional blocks with *The Weigh Forward*.

These are personal examples of other people's positive healing. If you experience a knee-jerk reaction of fear around loss or change when reading their changes, know you are safe and secure and in complete charge of what you choose to change in your life.

- Jackie was a self-confessed hoarder, and could never throw things away and organise her home. After losing weight with *The Weigh Forward*, she amazed herself with having a huge clear out of junk in the house.

- Since John's mother died ten years earlier, he still slept in the small back bedroom of his family farmhouse leaving her master bedroom like a shrine. Before losing weight he would say, 'She would turn in her grave if I moved anything.' As a fifty-year-old farmer with the whole place to himself, and after losing weight and understanding his issues with his mother, he eventually 'let go' of her influence and cleared out most of her stuff, redecorating the master bedroom and taking it over for himself. (To the subconscious this was a massive shift and had repercussions in all areas of his life. He was able to make strong decisions for himself rather than worry what his mother might think, which used to paralyse him to not act at all.)

- Paula's family used to eat at a small table in the lounge, and it regularly became a place of argument between her and her husband. Having lost weight and found value in herself, she had a huge showdown with her husband to decide if he could change and respect her more. The realisation he may actually lose her changed their relationship and, as a practical change, Paula created a larger eating space in their roomy kitchen and they started eating evening meals there, re-patterning judgement and argument into more loving meal times.

- Carl lost nearly three stone with *The Weigh Forward* and realised the only time he would get angry was in his car, experiencing 'road rage' at other drivers or traffic chaos. After understanding he could express his emotions in a more balanced way, he drove a different route to work each day, listening to a different radio station and patterned himself out of releasing his suppressed anger.

- Maureen, after following *The Weigh Forward* and dealing with her obsessive thoughts about staying thin, realised she had fallen into the habit of going around to her neighbour's house most days for a gossip. The gossip turned nastier over the years, judging other people in the street or friends about their weight. She was very open with her neighbour and explained the work she had done on herself and that she no longer wanted to judge others. Gradually she went over less and less until she had filled the time she spent there with more positive actions.

## Exercise

Create three sections in your Journal and decide on at least three achievable goals (one for home, people and daily habits) where you recognise a destructive circumstance or person and what you would choose to replace it with as part of your *The Weigh Forward* healing.

# DNA AND ENERGY VIBRATION

| HOME | |
|---|---|
| DESTRUCTIVE CIRCUMSTANCE | |
| DESIRED CHANGE | |

| PERSON | |
|---|---|
| DESTRUCTIVE INFLUENCE | |
| DESIRED CHANGE | |

| DAILY HABIT | |
| --- | --- |
| DESTRUCTIVE HABIT | |
| DESIRED CHANGE | |

# 19
## STICKING POINTS

The subconscious mind sees everything that we don't register consciously, but has no filter or rationale. When it comes to weight issues, a common example of this penchant for association is that often, when a person reaches a specific weight in stone which they cannot get below or keep going back to, it's because the subconscious is protecting that person from a difficulty or trauma they experienced at the correlating age.

Emily managed to lose a stone and a half, but whatever she tried, she could not get below twelve stone. Using *The Weigh Forward*, it was recognised that eleven was a very vulnerable age for her – she started a new school, had no friends and endured bullying. The subconscious associated twelve – and the weight of twelve stone – with the age, which had become a happier time for Emily by then. By keeping her from dipping below the safety of twelve stone, the subconscious was 'protecting' Emily. Using simple *The Weigh Forward* techniques, she was able to uproot her subconscious association and currently weighs just under ten stone.

For all my American clients, a similar subconscious association is set up with pounds, but taking the zero off, e.g.,160 lbs equals security of age sixteen and above, with the protection from vulnerable emotions at fifteen.

With certain subconscious quirks which I have labelled 'sticking points', it is important to recognise they are indications which help you build up the jigsaw of your full relationship and patterning with food, weight and image. Remember, the Core Emotional Block Visuali-

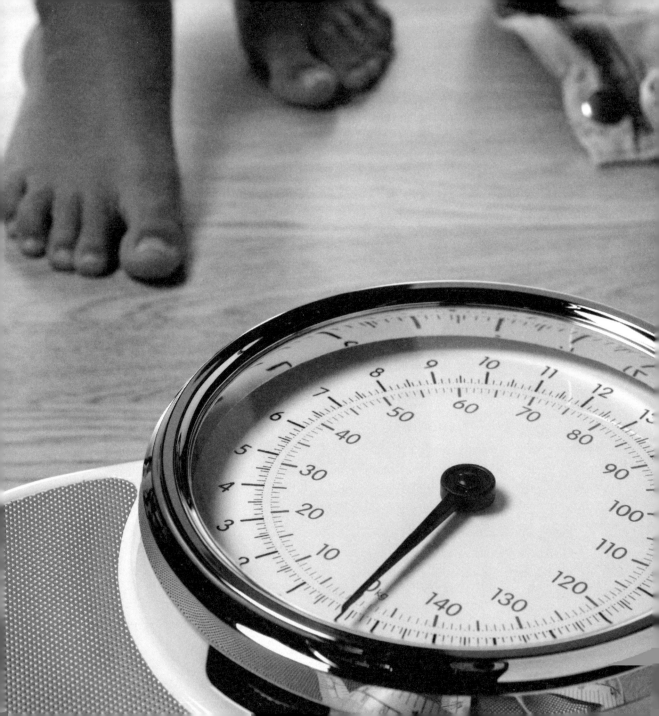

sation is where you get to the root of the issue and maximise your healing. An aspect, like sticking points, is helpful when someone starts to let go of the weight, then hits one of those times when weight no longer shifts – there is always a reason – and it may just be that in the past that was when your subconscious realised your will power and dieting was starting to have an effect, and would then sabotage to keep your 'protection' on. So, out of habit, it would automatically stop at a certain weight. For some people, the association gets lodged in the subconscious at a certain dress size, so 10, 12, 14, 16, 18, or 22 become sticking points for similar reasons.

When I immerse myself in people and their subconscious, as I do, I recognise patterns in everything, because I'm so conditioned to seeing how the subconscious is reacting. I have included a few more possible sticking points below to help you with recognising if there are any in your life.

1. A certain weight – remember, the sticking point will be the safety (the weight below where the trauma was).
2. A certain dress size.
3. A time of the year. Brian's father worked for a major corporation, and they moved each year. Every September he would start a new school and endure having to settle anew. He cleared the issues with his father being responsible for uprooting him from friends every year and being cold emotionally, but after losing a few stone got worried that, by August, he'd put another stone back on. His sticking point was his subconscious, twenty years later, still preparing him for having to go into emotional battle by starting a new school in September (even though he was a grown man of thirty-two).

4.  Seasons of the year – these can be quite common when a past life (or ancestral patterning) is stuck in a pattern of holding on to weight during the 'storing' winter months.
5.  Moving house.
6.  If parents visit a couple of times a year at certain times. Teresa would always put a stone on the few weeks before her parents flew over for their bi-annual visit. The patterning of needing the protection from the 'sly digs' and 'loaded barbs' was a sticking point for her subconscious. She turned the visits to her advantage. Having cleared the core blocks, she was able to reassure her subconscious each time they were coming, and politely picked her parents up whenever there was a sly dig and confront it there and then.
7.  Travelling / holidays – for any number of reasons, like fear of being laughed at again in a bikini, to fear of work not needing you while you are away, to fear of something happening to your family or home.

## Exercise

Make a note in your Journal of any physical sticking points (weight, dress size, etc.) and also any external sticking points (travel, visits, annual seasons, etc.) then write out an action plan of how you are going to reassure your subconscious and confront the sticking point the next time it is activated.

# 20

## HABITS, PATTERNS AND ROUTINES

The beauty of having undertaken your *The Weigh Forward* investigation and 'clearing', as part of this book, is knowing that there are so many situations and circumstances that you can now recognise as having some control over. To continue with the theme of your subconscious patterning and some examples that have been touched on in the previous few chapters, this chapter will look specifically at the habits, patterns and routines that may have been contributing to negative responses to food, weight and body image.

You may feel, with understanding what your trigger foods are and what timings during the day are your so-called danger zones, that some of this chapter is repetitive. The idea is all about layers, unravelling your daily thoughts, feelings and actions that literally have shaped not just your body, but also your world.

### The Safe Sludge Syndrome

Anyone who has struggled with weight issues, food cravings and any form of body dysmorphia, will know that thoughts themselves become very ingrained and are on a continual loop, feeding your actions. I can't stress enough in this book how the subconscious loves patterns and is far too comfortable repeating negative thoughts and actions – I call it the 'safe sludge syndrome'. It may be sludge but it knows what it is and expects no surprises from it. So without taking the time to manage and change our thoughts and our responses to those thoughts, we are stuck in a repetitive loop.

135

From the moment you wake up thoughts about what you are going to eat for that day, what to look forward to, maybe how you are going to try and 'be good' with food, maybe rolling over in bed and feeling disgusted with your belly, or your hips, rolls of fat on your love handles, for example, are setting the day up for continual self-punishment and deprivation. Deprivation, because of trying to avoid certain foods you may think will help lose weight, and self-punishment, because you are either denying yourself, thinking you are boring, noticing the weight hasn't shifted and all manner of clever attacks that we create for ourselves. This is why it is important to focus on your thoughts and your responses during a full day, ideally during a full week. We are conditioned by our daily life to focus our attention on what we have to do – get the kids up, get them to school, go to work, sort out bills for the house, tidy the house, check in on your family and other day to day actions that structure the majority of our lives. We are not conditioned to focus our attention on what we are thinking and what responses we have to those thoughts. They are predominantly unconscious, but that doesn't mean they don't have power, that they don't carry energy or that they aren't shaping our lives from behind the scenes, because they are.

> *'What we are today comes from our thoughts of yesterday, and our present thoughts build our life of tomorrow: our life is the creation of our mind. Your worst enemy cannot harm you as much as your own unguarded thoughts. But once mastered, no one can help you as much.'*
>
> The Buddha

*'All that you accomplish or fail to accomplish with your life is the direct result of your thoughts. You are today where your thoughts have brought you; you will be tomorrow where your thoughts take you.'*

James Allen

Your thoughts are the most powerful tool available to you and nobody can manage them better than you. With reference to our daily habits, patterns and routines, I am asking you to break down the thoughts and actions of your day and see what unconscious thoughts and actions you are allowing to sneak out. This is the perfect time to do this because you have, by now, cleared your core emotional block and have started embedding your affirmations. So from the moment you wake up, recognise what negative thoughts are sneaking in around food, weight and shape and halt them to replace them with your affirmations.

We are habitual people so your daily routine will be full of exactly that: routine; the way you shower and the order in which you wash your body, the way you dress, how you make your breakfast, how you eat your breakfast, how you get to work, how your working day unfolds, be it the way you greet people or the way you tidy your desk. The same goes for getting home and the evening routines. These routines are so embedded that you aren't conditioned to the thoughts going on behind them.

That is what you are looking at today and ideally over the next week. Question what you are thinking. Why you make certain choices and whether the habit serves you or not. For example:

- What are you thinking about as you are shaving?
- Do you eat breakfast sitting down or on the run?
- Do you travel by car, public transport or by foot? What fills your time and your thoughts as you travel?

- Do you eat lunch, how do you eat lunch, where do you eat lunch? What are you thinking about as you eat lunch?
- What drinks do you have during the day – which ones are habits, which do you crave? When you crave a drink, what are you feeling?

Researchers have found that the average person has around 50, 000 thoughts a day with 80 per cent of those being negative, so obviously the few prompting questions above won't even scratch the surface of what you are thinking. But they should, hopefully, motivate you to really dig deep and monitor your thoughts, responses and routines then be able to question whether they add positively to your life or not. Changing the thought for a positive affirmation, and changing your response and your routine to more positive ones, will make a vast difference.

## Exercise

1. Make a list of five destructive thoughts you had today about food, weight or body shape.
2. Make a list of five times you made a choice today because of negative thoughts on food, weight or body shape, choosing certain food, clothes, socialising etc.
3. Make a list of five of your daily routines that you would be happy to change.

## Visualisations

Affirmations are one of the most powerful ways to help re-pattern your subconscious; the use of visual imagery is another one. Visualisation is a word that covers many forms of creating pictures for your mind. In fact, the core emotional block clearing you are guided through in this book is a 'visualisation'. What we are focusing on now, in this chapter, is the power of the imagery you create in your mind to continually feed the subconscious – what you are now taking control of and wishing to create in your reality. We are multi-sensory beings and we all accept information and learn in slightly different ways. Some people respond so well to what they hear others say, and others are always creating imagery to complement what they are absorbing. In my experience nobody operates from only one of his or her senses. We all – in general – amalgamate them, to differing degrees. It is important to be aware of this because, again, nobody will know you better than yourself. The subconscious, however, is conditioned to respond to imagery. It looks for patterns in what you see around you and can pick up on all sorts of symbolic associations from images that you may not consciously recognise. This was why subliminal marketing was such a success, and also became tightly controlled, because of the fears of us being so easily susceptible to suggestion.

We are still exposed to manipulative suggestion every single day, with the many media outlets we interact with. It's just more blatant than subliminal now, and heavily relies on repetition. Part of you creating positive imagery for your self is again to take your control back, and choose the types of imagery you want your subconscious responding to, rather than having it forced on you. For the purposes of your journey on *The Weigh Forward* we are going to focus on three categories of visual imagery that you can use on a daily basis while you re-pattern your subconscious.

## The Replacement Picture

This is a simple, yet powerful, image for you to create in your mind of a positive 'you' at a healthy balanced weight, and in a relaxed and happy space. Mind programming techniques often get you to visualise yourself in a bikini or pair of shorts, glowing with health. As I said earlier, that won't override your emotional blocks, but is now fine in this instance because you are working from the inside out, and now is the time to focus on the mental level imagery. If you feel happy with the cliché of swimwear, that will work well, but do create a picture that you feel comfortable with and can truly see yourself as. The more you can build that picture, including your other senses of how it feels to be a healthy weight, and how the environment around you sounds and smells, the more it will add to the clarity for your subconscious.

Over the years I have had hundreds of clients throw out examples of other visuals they have read about and often vent their frustrations and disappointments at feeling they didn't work for them. Part of this is what I have discussed earlier and in the chapter on affirmations – the imagery is trying to override a deep-rooted subconscious block and the ingrained destructive beliefs of our self-worth, and previous emotional traumas are too powerful to allow positive pictures to lie over the top of this murky terrain.

However, having cleared your root emotional blocks and recognised exactly how your destructive pattern is set up and what your pattern is, it is the perfect time to use positive mental imagery and affirmation.

You aren't over-laying – you are starting afresh.

Remember, any negative daily thought you are dealing with now is a trigger because of a conditioned response, one that you can halt and replace. This is also why you don't have to stress about the semantics of shifting your image from black and white to colour, or where in your mind you see the picture and how large you see it – these techniques are NLP-oriented and over-lay driven.

Clients who have tried these techniques before finding out about *The Weigh Forward* often complain that, when it matters, they can't seem to picture their positive imagery. It is the same as trying to sip a mint tea to calm your stomach (your positive imagery), straight after over indulging with a hot curry (an un-cleared block). There is far too much unrest and struggle going on with the stomach, trying to digest the curry, for the mint tea to have much effect. However, if the mint tea is sipped on an empty stomach the effect is much more powerful.

## Exercise
Visualisation 4 – *Positive Image Visualisation*

## POSITIVE IMAGE VISUALISATION.
To access your visualisation visit www.theweighforward.com/visualisations or enrich your experience by downloading the app at the iTunes store from the link available from this same web page.

## Intuitive Image Boarding
Now that you have your replacement picture floating around at the forefront of your mind, it's also worth having a tangible image board that you can create and keep close to you most of the time. Intuitive image boarding is literally a collage of words and pictures that you have intuitively cut out of magazines, books or similar sources and placed on an A3 card in a seemingly random way. I call it 'intuitive image boarding' because, once you have prepared your materials, the choosing of imagery and consequent cut and pasting is deliberately done quickly to allow your intuition to drive it all forward.

Once you have your image board finished it is good to display it as prominently in your home or work for a couple of months while you are re-patterning. Obviously, for some people, they will be sensitive of others in their household seeing their board especially if a partner is part of the destructive pattern you are seeking to change. Work may also be too difficult for some people to display their board.

Many of my clients these days take a photo of their board and save it as a screensaver on their mobile, on their computer and / or on their iPad. They print a copy of the picture out too, to fit into their Journal. It is important to manage the fine line between being able to see your image board often enough, to balancing the sensitivities of those around you. However, if you are already thinking of lots of worries as to who might see your board, what they might think of it and other fears and judgements, check if those worries are residues of the block you have cleared, and, as part of your healing, start to speak up for yourself and expect co-operation from those around you.

Before you begin the exercise, though, answer the questions below.

1. Who am I worried about seeing my image board and why?
2. Where would I feel most comfortable displaying my image board and where would I feel most uncomfortable displaying it?
3. If I am honest with myself, if I want others to see it, what are my motivations behind what I expect from them? (Am I looking for approval? Am I using it as a go-between to create confrontation with a partner? Am I expecting ridicule to give myself permission to give up on doing it? Am I letting them know what I am doing so I don't have to tell them?)

## Exercise: Creating Your Intuitive Image Board

Allow yourself at least an hour where you can work on your image board undisturbed. Make sure you have at least one piece of A3 card, good scissors, some colour pens, some paper glue, a pile of magazines and books you are happy to cut images and words from, or similar – like postcards, old photos etc. Some of my 'arty' clients have painted on theirs, stuck on metal lettering, used pipe cleaners, bent into shapes and so on. Whatever works for you.

Before you begin, take a few deep breaths, breathing deeply into your tan tien, then sighing them away. (The tan tien is loosely translated as 'elixir field' and is an important focal point for internal meditative techniques. It usually refers to the physical centre of gravity located in the abdomen – about three finger widths below and two finger widths behind the navel.) Then ask in your mind that you connect to the highest healing for your highest good, for your image boarding to create the most positive collage to help you move forward; imagery which will create positive visuals for you, regarding weight, food and body image.

Flick through your magazines and other material and rip or cut out any imagery, words or symbols that resonate with you. Try not to deliberate too long over the pictures or words, or rationalise why they appeal to you; just cut them out. Once you have all the words and images you are happy with, start arranging them on your piece of card. Collage them however you want, but again don't deliberate too long. If you want to add positive words, sayings or affirmations in pen, or use other artistic techniques, that's fine too.

Once you have finished, smile to yourself, feel proud. Seriously, this is another example of you taking responsibility for your healing and taking action to help yourself move forward. You could read about the process a thousand times, but, as with the other exercises in this book that you have interacted with, you have done it, you and nobody else, and that experience is unique to you.

I want you to spend five minutes *now* staring at your image board and repeating in your mind, 'I now embrace positive change into my life.' Once you have done that, choose the place where you are going to keep your image board for the next two months, and take any photos of it that you want, if you are going to save the image elsewhere, to assist regular viewing and absorbing.

# 21

## EGREGORES AND UNDERSTANDING THE GROUP CONSCIOUSNESS

Most of this book has focused on you, your subconscious and your patterns and triggers, and rightly so. This chapter, though, is devoted to helping you understand the power of group thought forms, and the group consciousness, so it will help you recognise if there are outside influences which may have been holding you back or hindering your efforts to move forward.

An 'egregore' can be defined as a 'group thought form' which can assume the characteristics of having an effectiveness and an influence greater than the sum of its individual members. To quote Gaeten Delaforge:

> '*The egregore continually interacts with its members but only as long as they behave and act in line with its original aim ... If the process is continued a long time the egregore will take on a kind of life of its own, and can become so strong that even if all its members should die, it would continue to exist on the inner dimensions and can be contacted even centuries later, by a group of people prepared to live the lives of the original founders.*'

Major religion will be an obvious example; strictly adhered to martial arts a lesser one. Fanatical Chelsea football supporters live within one, and on a lighter note, any teenage kid today that identifies with the teddy boys of the 1950s can tap into and access identity, emotion, beliefs and stream of consciousness from the egregore that was the teddy boy movement. I don't want to dwell too much on the esoteric aspects of egregores for *The Weigh Forward* as they will probably be internet researchable – because over the last millennium, when it wasn't our 'group lesson' to grow, as it is now, esoteric knowledge was mostly restricted to cults, orders and sects with mysterious practices, ceremonies and specialist understanding of the group mind. This is why some people today venture into the occult, because they know it is possible to access ancient energy – an egregore. In popular culture, the *Mummy* films are basically taking the premise of a strong leader re-awakening both the Egyptian cults and ancient Chinese warriors. An important point is that much of an egregore's energy hangs around on the astral plane, where constructed thought forms 'live' and entities, energies and 'lower' level spirits can attach to it.

I felt this first hand when heavily involved in the martial arts. The style I was an instructor for had a Master and a constructed belief system that 'this is the way', so initiates could gain self-worth, confidence, sense of identity and achievement by being a member of the organisation. Even though verbal homage was paid to the development of self, it was actually structured so that your identity and worth was a result of the group and the master, not yourself.

They never knew I was intuitive and, building up to the time, I was going to leave them. I would see the students and grown men, who had been in the style for years, talk the same way, dress the same, holiday the same and that was just the minor part. The biggest was they had lost their sense of self-worth as individuals, fearful of leaving and not having an identity or a higher connection to anything other than the group; in essence they had stymied their spiritual connection. When I left I could feel the hooks of 'energy' from the astral plane (the egregore) trying to suck my belief system back in. Having the tools, though, it was easy to de-link from and release any attachment to the group.

Those qualities I have mentioned of self-worth, confidence, sense of identity and achievement being dependant on the group are a classic indication. It is worth asking yourself would you be fearful of not supporting your football team anymore, of leaving the corporation you work for, of using Reiki healing your own way and not as part of a system? Of being able to do without Buddhist practices or daily yoga, or anything that is group run and has a hold on you? Just to ask the question is very revealing.

## Exercise

1. Make a list of any slimming 'organisation' you have joined, any twelve-step programme you have committed to, diets that you follow or have followed, and any other groups that you are involved in or have even set up yourself. Then write down some of the beliefs of those groups, or rules you have to adhere to. Do they serve you anymore?

2. Make a list of any beliefs you were subjected to growing up by your parents, school, religious organisation, and the beliefs you may have adopted as a result of friendships, sports, work colleagues or living with someone. (These sayings, thoughts and beliefs may roll off your tongue or out into your mind because of habit, but may no longer serve you well.)

# 22

## SLIMMING DOWN YOUR HOME AND SLIMMING DOWN YOUR SHOPPING

I felt it was important to devote a chapter of *The Weigh Forward* to the connection between your home and your weight, and also what shopping habits have developed over the years as a misdirection or distraction from surfacing emotions. So many of my clients over the years have found that, as they start letting go of weight during *The Weigh Forward* programme, they have had major clear outs and changed things around the home (see Chapter 18).

It is always very telling to look at your shopping habits with a newly discerning eye, now that you have cleared your core emotional block. What you are looking for are the habituated, emotional quick fix shopping habits that before today you will have used – similarly to food – to distract yourself and suppress emotions; the act of 'getting' and resultant self-punishment that invariably follows. These days, when I talk of shopping, it covers all mediums from the local high street, to catalogues, online stores and ordering purchases from overseas. There are two aspects to look at when investigating this: both the items you shop for and the nature of when and how you shop.

### Items

A common pattern with people who have struggled with their weight in the past is to have a 'thing' for shopping for shoes. It is not surprising considering that clothes are a constant reminder of weight problems and, regardless of how much weight someone puts on, they can always wear their 'same size' pair of shoes. Shoes are a constant, something that isn't dependant on having lost weight, or feeling good. Because of this they can become a substitute, although, as we have already discovered, only for the short-term. Many people describe the negative thoughts surfacing as soon as they are out of the shop. 'Why did I have to buy those shoes, what a waste, I didn't need them.' Watches are something I have seen, many times, become the centre of someone's shopping attention too – mostly male clients – where, as with shoes, they are a constant. They won't have to sit in the cupboard if you put weight on and again, regardless of what size you are, you can still associate yourself briefly with James Bond and the latest racing car driver superstar – the subconscious thinking you may not be emerging out of the surf in your Speedos, but you can still have the same watch on your wrist. Jewellery is similar to watches, predominantly with women. Again it is something that you can wear regardless of your size and shape and it also subconsciously offers a distraction from your body shape, drawing people's attention to your hands and the rings on your fingers, or the chains around your neck, bracelets on your wrists or earrings in your lobes.

The above examples are some of the obvious ones, but there can be more subtle items people are drawn to because of subconscious associations, like maintaining a hairstyle or type of clothes because it reminds you of happier times (which is why many people dress from a nostalgic habit rather than adhering to fashion).

## How And When You Shop

We covered certain food shopping when talking about trigger foods in Chapter 7 but there are also other shopping habits that can reveal emotional suppression too. For example, whenever Sadie was challenged in work or by friends about not knowing something, she didn't even realise that as soon as she could take a break she would be in the local bookshop in the self-help section, buying another book. Although it sounds obvious, she was unaware that her subconscious was punishing her every time for being stupid by buying a book with someone else's knowledge and wisdom, someone else telling Sadie what to do. Katie had a similar pattern with any comment about her looking tired, or scruffy, or unwell. She would be racing to the newsagent's and buying glossy magazines which made her feel worse, compared to all the airbrushed beauties, and better, for the flaws in celebrities exposed by the gossip magazines.

Sometimes it is not the specific association with what you are buying, but the very act of distraction. Ryan used to spend hours browsing and searching for books to buy from Amazon, to distract him from suppressed emotions of loneliness. James used to buy and sell things on eBay, 'to win approval ratings', and Finn used to collect memorabilia to feel a connection with those he aspired to. These are just a few examples to help understand what you are buying, and when you buy it. The exercise below helps you delve deeper into your own habits.

## Exercise

1.  Make a list of the different ways you shop or browse for shopping and what type of products / items you are constantly drawn to.
2.  Write down where you identify you use shopping as an emotional suppression and what shopping for these items is compensating for.

# 23

## THE PHYSICAL LEVEL – ACTION

I mentioned at the start of this book that the weight loss industry focuses predominantly on the physical and only two aspects of the physical at that – diet and exercise. What I meant is that yes, there is a relevance of intake of food and expenditure of calories, but for those choices to be successful, other levels have to be dealt with first. Those levels we have covered, and are covering comprehensively in this book. The full importance of the physical can be characterised more with the words *action* and *doing*. Taking responsibility for your actions and actually doing them is an integral part of your healing.

I mentioned earlier that we can't overly rely on one nature of our existence (emotional, mental, physical or spiritual) to deal with life. I have seen it time and time again – people who start opening up spiritually, going around and forgiving all the perceived wrongs against them before actually forgiving themselves.

If we take the most common pattern of father abandonment, we can clear the core emotional trauma of that initial event. We can spiritually forgive the subsequent destructive male relationships that followed, but however much we emotionally clear it, we mentally understand it and we spiritually work on it, there is a key ingredient missing – *the physical breaking of that habit.* Unless the person dealing with self-worth issues in male relationships physically takes action and speaks up, sets a boundary, confronts, or any other form of actually doing something in the physical world with the physical person pressing the buttons, the pattern won't change. It is *that* important.

Everyone reading this book will have to at some stage to confront his or her fears in a physical situation and physically take action in that physical situation.

For example, Beatrice went through classic father abandonment at age seven when her dad left and she consequently had little contact with him. As we have outlined earlier (and you should by now be recognising more easily) it meant Beatrice as an adult does everything for the men in her life, and previously has allowed them their destructive behaviour. Over the years she has gone out with men who wouldn't commit, men who were absent for long periods of time because of work or choice, men who were verbally abusive, men who were violent and men who would sulk at the slightest thing. These men could well have ranged from five foot to six and a half feet tall; they could have been rich, poor, intelligent and stupid – what I am saying is that, regardless of how different they may have seemed on the outside, they are actually all the same, and Beatrice's behaviour towards them was exactly the same. All those men taught Beatrice to feel vulnerable to losing out on love because of going away, bullying, sulking, cheating or whatever other emotional form of control they used – and Beatrice allowed the behaviour because of her fears.

Whatever her excuses, she realised during *The Weigh Forward* that her low self-worth meant she daren't lose out on love again so she did everything for those men to make them love her. She never 'rocked the boat' in terms of disagreeing with them, and allowed them their controlling behaviour. Beatrice, after clearing and healing her past, reached a point in her development where she valued herself enough to start the process of physically changing her experiences in the world.

I have to explain a little deeper here that our thoughts do create our reality, but remember that your outside world will start adjusting to your more positive thoughts, and that will require adjustment of your interactions with people. I have discovered over the years that it is probably best not to tip-toe when it comes to understanding your change. By following *The Weigh Forward* programme you are once and for all looking to understand your subconscious and finally let go of weight or the repetitive thoughts around food and image. To do that, your daily circumstances will have to be shaken up in order for you to include more positive experiences in your life, and that includes a shake-up of relationships.

If your weight (like the example of Beatrice above) protects the suppressed anger from feeling undervalued and unappreciated by your boyfriend or husband, then once you re-pattern your subconscious into valuing yourself and no longer fearing abandonment then obviously it has to shake up the current relationship. What does that mean? Everyone always thinks of the worst-case scenario (the deepest fear) that the relationship will end. So, before we know it, we fear making changes and remain unable to fully let go of the excess weight.

There is no textbook response from individuals, because everyone is a result of their unique compilation of experiences and beliefs. One thing is certain, though, if you change then your partner will get their buttons pressed and will subconsciously be fearful and vulnerable in some way too. I say there is no textbook response because some of my clients have had frank conversations with their partner who have been completely understanding, and unaware that all these strong emotions had been affecting their wife / husband. For others, it has meant the end of the relationship because, as with the example of Beatrice, it was easier for the boyfriend to move on and continue with his lazy attitude to change, than to own his bullying and controlling tactics. It is worth remembering that everyone has emotional blocks and uses different destructive patterns to try and get through life if they don't work on them.

Beatrice's last boyfriend had witnessed his mum having an affair then experienced how betrayed his dad felt. To protect himself he was subconsciously choosing women he could control and didn't 'love' too deeply so he wouldn't have to experience that pain of betrayal. Obviously, unless Beatrice's boyfriend had been willing to clear his emotional blocks, he wouldn't like Beatrice speaking up for herself and valuing herself – it would make him feel vulnerable.

It is amazing how everyone who starts to work on themselves and follows *The Weigh Forward* programme completely understands what self-worth and abandonment issues they have cleared and are changing, and yet when it comes to speaking up for themselves or setting boundaries on a physical level, they come up with all manner of delaying tactics or justifications.

That is why I thought I would get the bottom line out early – you will have to confront some people in your life now, you will have to speak up for yourself in a possibly uncomfortable situation and you may have to come out of or lose a relationship (a marriage / girlfriend or a family member). You may even have to experience the possibility of losing a job. If that sounds dramatic, well, it's more a case of sometimes, to achieve a serious shift, it requires confronting serious shift – without the 'f'.

In many cases clients face those fears and their transition is actually very smooth. An understanding partner may be very empathetic to how they had been feeling; a boss may actually respect the person for speaking up and promote them instead of sacking them. However, what I have noticed is this: those who are prepared to face their fears and, come what may, stick up for themselves and physically take action to change the pattern are rewarded the most.

For both guys, it was an enormous step for them, considering their fears of not being loved and issues of low self-worth, to end a relationship. It was a real testament to them that they had embraced their subconscious work and really wanted to move on out of fear once and for all. With Robert, his girlfriend came back to him a few weeks later not just saying that she missed him and wanted to get back with him, but that she realised she had been spending more – almost pushing him to get rid of her – so she could punish herself once again (remember, everyone has their emotional blocks which shape their story).

Just because I gave a couple of examples of how situations changed smoothly, you can't give yourself false strength by taking tough action while subconsciously crossing your fingers that it works out OK, because that again is reverting to subconscious fear. For example, I worked with Robert and Andrew in a similar period of time. Robert, in clearing his emotional blocks, realised he had to set a boundary on his girlfriend's spending (she spent thousands on his credit card, always threatening to leave if he tried to discuss his financial worries with her, saying she obviously wasn't worth it). He set a boundary of £300 per month for her and said if she ignored that she was disrespecting his wishes and not valuing him. This was a big thing for Robert, but he realised his fear of losing his girlfriend had been controlling him, getting him into debt and making him depressed. The very first month she ignored it and Robert ended the relationship.

Andrew had a similar situation, but his girlfriend was always going out 'with the girls' and flirting with men. She hadn't had an affair but craved that attention and said kisses were harmless fun. After clearing his emotional blocks, Andrew explained that he loved her, it was fine for her to see her girlfriends but kissing someone else was not valuing him. His girlfriend tried for a week or so but was soon back to her old ways. Robert ended the relationship. With Andrew, although he had made the decision to end the relationship, he sneakily expected his girlfriend to 'realise how lucky she had been and come back'. That was the key difference between Robert and Andrew; Robert had no expectation of his girlfriend coming back whereas Andrew did. Their examples don't mean that if you have to confront something and you truly mean it then it will work out. It is just a good example of taking action with an acute awareness of what your subconscious expectations are. (There is an exercise in the next chapter that expands on those sneaky subconscious expectations.)

# 24
## CONFRONTATION

Confrontation: a good, controversial word which conjurs images of arguments, fear, worry, insecurity, vulnerability, and leaves an all round general bad taste in the mouth. I mean 'confrontation' in terms of physically having to break patterns once you have cleared the core emotional block. It is 'confrontation' in terms of literally saying a gentle word to somebody or making a new household rule. Confrontation obviously can be defined as hostility or defiance, but it also means to present for acknowledgement, or to bring together for examination or comparison or just to stand facing each other. Those latter definitions are not aggressive or fearful connotations of the word. They are actually tools for taking action and breaking a pattern.

I have broken down confrontation into two main categories for you to work with as part of your *The Weigh Forward* programme: your *main confrontation* and your *daily confrontation*.

### The Main Confrontation
When you follow my guided visualisation to clear your core emotional block within the subconscious, the main event that you have revisited will definitely benefit from a physical confrontation of predominantly the person involved and also a specific place. By clearing the block you have cellularly removed the 'virus' from your subconscious. Your other tools, including the one of *ceremony*, will help complete closure while the other exercises in-

cluding *affirmations* and *visualisations* will help re-pattern. To physically confront the main event will complete the circle of both closure and re-patterning.

This main confrontation may be having an open and frank conversation with a father who left the family home or was abusive in some way. It may involve releasing a secret about the emotional trauma you suffered. It may entail you reconnecting with an estranged child because your parent has died and you have become your own father / mother by creating a circumstance of estrangement. It may involve you looking up and trying to arrange a meeting with a teacher, a priest or the school bully. This is the 'uncomfortable' feeling our subconscious will try and avoid, but one that is integral to your completion of healing and the ability for the body to finally let go of weight.

In preparation for your main confrontation I recommend the three following steps:

1. Write a letter to the person you are releasing for your main confrontation. You don't have to send this letter; you could burn it or decide to bring it with you to the 'meeting' but it actually helps you to release those residues of your emotional hurts, and will give you clarity for the most important thing you feel you have to say.

2. This main confrontation is all about you and taking responsibility for your hurts and, to use a spiritual cliché, 'reclaim your power'. The outcome is not the reason for this confrontation. You are not expecting hugs, cuddles, kisses, eternal apologies, contrition, and lifelong pleas of 'how can I ever make it up to you'. No, you are looking to be able to explain how you felt (not how they made you feel), and to set a boundary of how you expect their relationship or non-relationship with you to unfold in the future.

3. The venue for the main confrontation should ideally be in public; a quiet café,

bar or restaurant where you can sit together, a place you have no history of and, if you want a third party there for support, that is helpful too. The way of handling 'closure' through your main confrontation I touched on in the previous point, but will reiterate here. This isn't about blame. You will have spent a lifetime blaming them and blaming yourself. (You are blamed out!) This isn't about anger because you have spent a lifetime suppressing angry emotions and this isn't about approval because your subconscious will have spent your lifetime dreaming of winning love and approval or achieving something to 'show the bastard'.

## This Is About You And Only You

If you have any other sneaky subconscious goal or aspiration it will hinder a clear and powerful confrontation for you. I stress powerful, because this is the first time in your life when you can speak up for yourself and set a boundary of what is acceptable behaviour and / or interaction for you and what is not, and what the consequence of unacceptable behaviour will be.

That way you can complete your healing regardless of how the other person involved receives the information or reacts to it. Anything the other person says to argue, manipulate, move the goal posts, excuse or try to blame etc., is not the point of the exercise. This is why I mention it is not about blame or anger.

It is about you calmly and forcefully explaining how you felt,
and what is now acceptable to you.

158

Here are some examples of a few of my client's main confrontations:

- Sarah's uncle had abused her as a child. Her mother had brushed it under the carpet. She confronted her mother saying how she felt let down by her for not sticking up for her and that she was no longer going to allow her mother to continually say things along the lines of 'don't be so silly'. Even now, if Sarah said she wanted a new piece of furniture or was thinking of going on holiday her mother would quip 'don't be so silly, you don't need another settee', or 'don't be so silly you don't need to go there on holiday'. If her mother, in the future, dismissed her in such a way Sarah would say, 'I haven't invited you to put me down or dismiss me,' and ask her to leave or hang up the telephone if it was during a phone call. This is an excellent example of where such a serious issue of abuse by a male relative had filtered down to daily dismissals from a mother. (Sarah's uncle had died but even if he hadn't, she had already confronted him and had no contact.) The current festering issue was Sarah's feelings of worthlessness from her mother. (After working with *The Weigh Forward,* Sarah actually became a mother herself for the first time because of her subconscious dealing with her own mother issues.)
- Angela, after years of denying it was important to find her birth father, tracked him down. Again in working with the Main Confrontation, she had no gilded expectations, just the release of being able to say this was how she felt growing up. As it so happened, they got on really well. She found out the hidden heartbreak her father had gone through (a mental breakdown just before she was born) and they remained in contact.
- David had such suppressed anger with his father, but when his father died un-

159

expectedly his weight ballooned again because he had always felt 'I'll make him proud' then subconsciously realised he couldn't. By working through *The Weigh Forward* he realised he had created the same estrangement from his own son. Although ten years earlier his son had said he didn't want to see him anymore, David had just accepted the situation and kept piling on the weight, protection from all his self-hatred, as being like his own father and the lack of love. David met up with his son, not to plead to see him but just explain his own situation with his father and how he felt about not seeing his son, and how deep down David now knew he was a good person and could be a good father. Although his son still didn't want to see David after that, it had been vitally important for David to confront his son and finally let go of his self-punishment. He is now hopeful about the future, always sending cards and letters to his son to let him know he loves him and is there for him.

I use these three examples because David and Angela met their son and their father in a public place, whereas for Sarah, she wanted to meet her mum back at the house where her uncle had abused her as a child. New owners currently lived there but they sat in the car outside and that helped Sarah also let go of the negative hold the area had over her. After she had confronted her mother, she walked around the street reassuring herself how safe and secure she now was in her life. I have thousands of other examples and, although some may be very similar, they are unique. There is a real need for discernment and complete honesty with yourself in recognising, after your core emotional clearing, who it is you need to confront. I say discernment because some of my clients have actually confronted their main person. Others have found that they can't find theirs, or the person refuses all approaches for contact.

The most difficult part of writing a book that tries to reach so many people is that there is a decision which you have to reach, using that honesty and discernment yourself. With all my clients it has always worked out the best way for that person, in terms of who they have their main confrontation with, or how it unfolds. Remember, on a spiritual level your actions will be rewarded and are for your highest good, so an opportunity will present itself even if it is not the original person you thought you needed closure with.

## Steps To Narrowing Down Your Confrontation Focus

During your core emotional block visualisation there will have been a main person involved in your emotional event. Below are a series of questions to lead you to the main person for your confrontation.

1. Is the main person still alive?
2. If not, is there another person close to you who you have suppressed emotions from for not understanding what you went through, or not sticking up for you during that time? For example, a father who used to verbally abuse you and judge you for being promiscuous or dressing promiscuously may have died, but is there a deep-rooted anger at your mother for not sticking up for you?
3. If the main female or male protagonist is no longer alive / unwilling to meet you / untraceable, move on to the next male / female relationship that mattered but where those same themes of abandonment and self-worth were an issue. When confronting that person do ensure that you have already completed the *confrontation visualisation part 1* below.
4. Who would you want to bring with you for support (someone to make you feel safe but stay in the background and not interfere with your confrontation and healing)?

5.  Is the venue of your emotional event somewhere that holds negative thoughts and emotions for you and still affects how you feel, if you are in that area or near that place now, as an adult? If so, try and arrange for the meeting to be there. If the other person can meet you but not at the negative venue (playground, church, old house, etc.) arrange to visit that place again, following the *confrontation visualisation part 2.*

## CONFRONTATION VISUALISATION PART 1&2.

To access your visualisation visit www.theweighforward.com/visualisations or enrich your experience by downloading the app at the iTunes store from the link available from this same web page.

## Location

I want to clarify, when I talk of the venue, the location or the area, it requires the discernment I talked of earlier because there are two factors taking place here. Your own investigation should help you decide whether it is purely about the person you need to confront or if the venue / location / area where a certain emotionally traumatic event occurred holds as much weight negatively in the subconscious, and needs confronting and letting go too. Obviously you may choose to have your main confrontation first (a neutral venue in a public place) and then have some form of release of all your negative associations with the venue, or in some cases to do them both together.

For example, Jody got run over by a bus when she was a seven-year-old child, and for years her mother said it was her fault. Jody carried that feeling for years. During her regression visualisations, as part of *The Weigh Forward* programme, she saw that the bus had ridden the kerb and clipped her before she stepped out. Regardless of it not being her fault, having been left by her mother to walk home alone, her mother had projected her guilt by blaming her. Jody took her mother to the same roadside spot where the accident happened and explained how she felt, that she had not done anything wrong and how she had given herself a hard time by feeling worthless and stupid. (For years Jody was over cautious and almost pedantic about daily life.) She confronted her mother, expressing how she felt (not blaming) and importantly set the boundary that she wouldn't allow any more disparaging comments. In this instance it was also important to let go of the area where it had happened because her mother still lived in the same town where Jody grew up. Although Jody now lived miles away, she visited her mother regularly, always took her into town and felt emotional going past the accident spot (see *confrontation visualisation part 2*).

Some other examples of areas / locations that my clients have reconciled:

- Revisiting a childhood home even though new people live there
- Returning to a holiday venue where they had experienced trauma as a child
- Visiting their old school (the school hall where they were laughed at on stage / the school sports field where they 'messed up' / the school changing rooms where they were embarrassed / the playground where they were bullied)
- Returning to their father's old place of work
- Moving back to their childhood town and reconciling the area where they used to play 'naughty' games as children
- Returning to the 'home' country the family emigrated from when they were born

- Revisiting the house of the child they used to play with down the road
- The old café in their hometown where they had seen their dad kissing another woman
- The railway bridge where their friend had been killed in a tragic childhood accident
- Revisiting the hospital where they were left in an incubator as a newborn / had an operation as a child

## Daily Confrontation

Although I obviously use the phrase 'Daily Confrontation', this is the vital daily recognition of old triggers and the physical action of being able to speak up for yourself in the moment (whether being able to say 'no' or telling a partner what it is you want to do, or expressing how disrespectful you feel someone's actions are towards you).

Once you have cleared your core emotional block and recognised what your destructive pattern was, and what your plan of action is for re-patterning, it is amazing how many 'opportunities' arise during the day for you to take action. You have stated intent to your subconscious to change and you have started to shift the memory in your own DNA. It is during this change that your outside world will reflect what you are looking at, creating situations that give you the chance to take action to prove to the subconscious that you do value yourself, and no longer have to fear being rejected.

Many clients feel literally lighter from having undergone *The Weigh Forward* clearing visualisations and understanding what they had been subconsciously suppressing and reacting to all these years. However, the daily confrontations are sometimes all too easy to ignore, because the initial leap of feeling better has already happened. It is imperative that you are seen by the subconscious as living the truth you are affirming to it on a daily basis. If you are now stating with your affirmations 'I now love, value and approve of myself' and are then in a situation where your partner ignores you or dismisses what you are saying, that is the exact time for one of your daily confrontations. Stop the conversation and ask calmly why he / she was choosing to ignore what you were saying. It is the same for the example I used of the person in the shop serving the person behind you in the queue. Right there in that moment just speak up and say, 'Excuse me I was first.' You'll be amazed how many people would 'let it ride' by not wanting to cause a scene, or by pretending it is no big deal as they weren't in a hurry anyway. Not true. All the subconscious will note here is that you allowed complete strangers to have their needs met before yours. The simple act moves mountains in the subconscious, reaffirming through physical demonstration that you do indeed love, value and approve of yourself.

I have included some examples below, both seemingly major and also what you could perceive as flippant, where clients have had daily confrontations.

- Telling your male boss that you actually take care of many things behind the scenes so feel it is unfair of him to shout at you because he has lost his report. You didn't.
- Asking your partner if you could both go to the restaurant you fancied as opposed to meeting his friends down the pub ... again!
- Reminding your father that, yes, you are proud of your brother but also proud of yourself for raising two wonderful kids and keeping a beautiful home.
- Letting your clients know that from next month your appointments for your reiki / reflexology / healing or whatever are going to be for an hour and cost *x* amount of pounds. (It is common when dealing with self-worth issues on *The Weigh Forward* to be a healer and offer far too much of your time for little or no charge.)

- Telling your husband that, no, your new blouse wasn't in the sale, you paid £50 for it and it is worth every penny and you feel you deserve it. (Again this is important as so many clients feel they can only justify buying something for themselves if it was in the sale, or cheap – remember what this tells the subconscious: you are a cheap, second-hand person who doesn't deserve something nice.)
- Telling your partner that his mother can come around for Sunday dinner, but for the next few Fridays you are having time for yourself to catch up on some books you wanted to read and films you wanted to watch.

The above examples are just snippets of the kind of daily confrontations you may encounter, and most of them highlight how a large issue of father abandonment trickled down into everyday life with how your boss or partner interacts with you.

## Exercise

Having read this chapter on taking physical action and confrontation complete the following two tasks:

1. Decide who your main confrontation is going to be with, write your letter first then decide if you would like to give that person your letter or burn it. Is the venue relevant or do you only need to meet in a safe public place? Finally call or write to the person requesting the meeting and arrange a time. For some people they may talk and see their mother regularly so it is in fact very easy to set up a meeting for the main confrontation; however you may be facing resistance from your subconscious by contacting someone from your past, and having an expla--

nation for them to understand before you even meet them. Honesty is the best approach and keep it condensed, by being able to say that you have been looking over your life lately and want to let this person know how you felt about a situation in the past that will help you move on. You don't have any agenda; purely a wish to meet up and explain your own feelings, and that will really help.

2. Make a list of what you feel were opportunities for daily confrontations in the past, then make a list of ten daily confrontations you are prepared for now.

## Sneaky Subconscious Expectation

I know I alluded to good old sneaky expectations earlier, but I'm going to expand on the types of subconscious expectations and possible subconscious sabotages in more depth here, to remind us how wily the subconscious can be in playing along with us, then, before we know it, dressing up the old pattern in a different way. If we take the issue of your *main confrontation* first, it is vital to remember that this is a powerful thing for you to do to help on your journey of losing weight. To the subconscious, though, it is trying to protect you from previ-ous vulnerable emotions – especially considering your *main person* is linked to your *main emotional block*. As a result, the excuses for not following through your *main confrontation* will come thick and fast from your subconscious, as well as the sneaky expectations.

Excuses like, 'My father has Alzheimer's, so what's the point as he won't remember what I'm saying.' (He doesn't have to as this is about you and expressing how you feel.) Or, 'My adoptive family are stressed at the moment so not a good time to look up my birth parents.' (I'm sorry but there is no ideal time; there is usually always something going on with people and all we do in this situation is again put our own needs on the backburner.)

There are many types of sabotage, but at the end of the day they are just that – sabotage – whether they run along the lines of 'I can't be bothered having to deal with my mother's guilt trip', or 'my husband won't like it if I upset my father', or 'I'll wait until my mum has her holiday so she isn't so stressed'. All of them will either be a delaying excuse, or a paranoid excuse. 'This is bonkers, why do I want to rake up the past?' All these are still sabotage, because you are definitely not bonkers, you don't give a monkey's what they think and you are a grown woman/man with a confidante by your side, and they can get as mad as they want in their own world, but you are not being controlled by their fear any longer. This is the upshot of what you are embarking on. You have been unhappily overweight for a long time and have decided that your health, happiness and well-being has moved up from the bottom of the list to the top and requires serious addressing.

I am obviously not advocating a meeting in cases where there is the possibility of violent or aggressive behaviour towards you, but these are few and far between.

Even if it is a possibility, somehow and in some way, you have to gain your voice

If we are moving on to serious situations, I have had clients who have asked the law for help, those who have started legal proceedings and those who have faced down the bully. I am certainly not saying it is easy, but I am saying the issues will not go away, and the control of fear will only get worse. It seems all too easy in these days of political correctness to play down our ability to speak up for ourselves but you will be surprised that the very fact you have taken action to speak up for yourself will release a metaphorical (and literal!) weight.

## Exercise

Write down all the delaying and paranoid excuses that have run through your mind since you decided to set up your *main confrontation* meeting, lightly cross them out in your Journal, then write at least three positive paragraphs starting with the following phrase. My main confrontation is a very positive thing for me; it is helping me to  _____

_____

Make an honest list of any sneaky expectations you may have regarding your main confrontation. Be searingly honest with yourself, by seeing how you feel with different outcomes playing out in your mind. There is absolutely no harm in visualising the meeting going well; you are just making sure you don't subtly shift the power from your own actions over to needing a certain response or action from the other person.

THIS IS ABOUT YOU!

# 25
## SPIRITUAL EGO

'Spiritual ego' is a phrase I coined to know quickly in a visual sound-byte what was going on with certain clients with weight problems. I mean 'spiritual ego' in terms of an imbalanced spiritual responsibility for others.

> Father (father, father figure or God) abandonment = imbalanced spiritual responsibility for others, divided by low self-worth.

This is a scenario that became apparent to me over the years. Because somebody went through the emotional trauma of a key father abandonment in some way, their subconscious felt that it was their fault and they were not worthy of that person's love. That subconscious feeling of it being far too painful to have to revisit again sets up the pattern of spiritual ego, where the person who suffered decides to become the rescuer, helper, mother, enabler (to use a few common words) and 'heal the world'. Their experience of healing the world is to try and make it better for everyone around them so they will be loved and approved and, as a result, become invaluable to others and never abandoned again.

That is the plan anyway but, as we all realise, it doesn't work out like that because ultimately suppressing emotion is unhealthy and leads to discordance in the body and, eventually, we have to deal with it – but probably not before the pattern of spiritual ego has infected the person's personal life, their work and their drive.

I have mentioned earlier about the father abandonment link to consequent male relation-ships, but, as the weight of the suppressed emotions increases, the fear of not being loved and approved of permeates every aspect of a person's life. For example, Tanya was six stone over-weight and exhausted in her life. Following *The Weigh Forward* programme, she cleared her core emotional block of her abusive alcoholic father.

What also became apparent were the tell tale signs of this spiritual ego. Tanya found it very difficult to:

- Be on her own and, especially, be on her own without distraction. If she had any time on her own she would be either baking food for somebody, or trying to telephone, text or e-mail them, to see if they were OK. If she couldn't get hold of somebody, she would watch television until she fell asleep.
- Be balanced about birthdays and memorable dates. She was fastidious about remembering people's birthdays and would put an immense amount of thought and love into getting the right card and present, even though she often couldn't afford to.
- Talk about herself or ask for help or advice on anything.
- Do anything for herself. Even going shopping usually involved helping an elderly neighbour do their shopping while she grabbed a few essentials for herself. As for a holiday for herself – out of the question.

These few examples are classic signs of spiritual ego. Before you berate me for being a spoilsport for thinking that this 'angel' Tanya, who sounds so lovely, was doing anything wrong, I am obvi-ously not suggesting we don't love our neighbours and give to others. I am saying, though: make sure you aren't doing it just to be loved because, as Tanya discovered, it becomes a never ending monster consuming your every thought, driving your every action.

Tanya was suppressing daily anger when her little voice inside was quietly saying 'what about me'. Her weight steadily ballooned over the years regardless of numerous attempts at diets and every time, for example, some people forgot her birthday or just scribbled a quick card, she would feel more worthless again. All her subconscious heard, by her doing every-thing for everyone else and worrying about everyone else, was that she was worthless and last on a long list of everyone else who was more important than her. It was easy for Tanya to see her pattern of spiritual ego and, having cleared her core emotional blocks, it was a lot easier to set aside time for herself each day to do nothing. She could still send cards, but in a balanced way and also reduce her worry about needing to be in contact with people constantly. She would just catch herself needing to call someone, reassure how loved she was, and let go of the knee-jerk reaction to having a spare minute for herself.

## Is Your Job Or Your Role Keeping You Fat?

Tanya's need to be needed and loved by others was so strong that she was drawn to the caring industry, starting off as a nurse, then changing jobs until she was looking after mental health patients. In a clinical way, her subconscious has kept challenging her to do more and more for others for less and less validation, love and approval. I am not going to tip-toe here. This isn't about the altruism of the caring industry or it being the job of angels. I'm sticking up for the minority of people who are actually punishing themselves by doing such a job. And boy, do they need sticking up for!

Tanya came to that realisation. She herself had committed twenty years of her life to the job, watched her pay and appreciation reduce, and the selfless expectation increase. She no longer took any joy from the job and felt guilty for wanting to leave and do something else. Realising she was tentatively nurturing her fragile self-worth back up again, she deserved to act for once in her life in a way that felt right for her.

Many healers and so-called psychics and mediums are actually stuck in their own spiritual ego. It is difficult to confront this topic and very easy for people to get defensive or miss the point. I am not making a judgement on people who are healers and psychics / mediums, but it is important to recognise how, for some people, it becomes a great excuse and distraction to avoid dealing with their own emotional hurts and subconscious blocks. I have met hundreds of healers and psychics and, being a very clear intuitive myself, can speak from experience.

In random examples where there has been a traumatic father abandonment or an abusive childhood or an emotionally cold parent, we already understand how a person's self-worth drops and the subconscious puts everyone else's needs before their own. What a perfect profession to be drawn to, the healing industry! Try and solicit the love and 'need' of other people by helping them, and distract yourself from your own emotional stuff. The problem is that we are only able to heal to the level of where our own healing has taken us. For many healers they are limited in their ability and also will end up attracting clients to press their buttons or reflect their own dramas back at them – that is not healing. That is joint support and empathy, and also means the healer 'projinks' (projects their own thoughts) because they are too consumed by their own reference points of emotional hurt.

The caring and healing industries fill the criteria for some people to be subconsciously drawn to them, because it means they can get busy with other people's dramas and not have to deal with their own. It also means the pattern of being a good little boy / girl to try and win parental love so they don't abandon you just turns into trying to heal the world.

Trying to be invaluable to others to validate self-worth will always run risks. Self-worth will never be fulfilled outside of yourself, only ever from within.

With psychics and psychic mediums, there is often the same underlying experience of a father abandonment of sorts but also, very often, a deep-rooted subconscious belief of having been abandoned by God. We have two things going on in these instances: the initial father abandonment and subsequent weight gain from suppressed anger, and the 'need to be needed' pattern that develops to try and avoid not being loved by others (father). Also, in many cases I have witnessed, the trauma of abandonment was so painful that the person 'drifts off' in times of fear and sadness and starts tapping into other realms of the spirit. (Because it is too painful dealing with people and everyday life, it's much nicer to go and play with the angels!)

There is a lot to digest here and I may be taking for granted information that you may not have yet considered. In my understanding I believe implicitly in the 'soul' and that we have lived many lives. I also believe implicitly in other levels of existence, ranging from stuck spirits and negative entities, through ascended master consciousness, all the way up to God.

These are all intangible realms and require a sensitivity and heightened intuition to 'tap' into. By the way, we are all thoroughly capable of developing such awareness and intuition, and therein also lies the problem, because when I talk of letting their minds wander in depression or during emotionally fearful and sad times and 'drifting off', people start to feel and see in their minds, or hear messages from these other planes of existence.

That is all very well, and actually no big deal, but what is a big deal is that people start tapping into these energies without understanding exactly what they are tapping into; without protecting their energies, without being clear of what they choose to tap into. Which is like discovering you can fly to another country and jump on a plane, land in New York and wander into Brooklyn taking whatever is offered and allowing anyone to interact with you. There is no way you would do that in reality, so why do people do it in other planes of existence? Because of ignorance and because of the need to be needed it means everyone else's needs are more important than one's own and that belief continues into our spiritual lives as well.

It may sound like a contradiction that some psychics are drawn to work with spirits and yet have a pattern of abandonment by God. But that is exactly part of what contributes to that person's suppressed anger and holding on to weight. For example, Violet was nineteen stone when she came to see me and a so-called 'celebrity' medium. During the process of *The Weigh Forward* we cleared Violet's core emotional block of losing her father when she was six and also, doing her timeline, she recognised that she had put on three stone quite quickly in the late 90s when she had started hearing her first messages from spirits. She admits that at the time she was depressed after her fiancée had broken off their engagement, and was searching for something. She went to a spiritualist church to be told she had a connection (we all do) and had started trying to hear messages. As soon as she started giving these messages to people, she put on lots more weight. We cleared a past life for her where she had been a nun in the 1600s and had been killed for her beliefs. Her soul, at the end of that life, felt she had sacrificed everything and devoted her life to God, only for him to let her die. This abandonment was triggered with her own father dying, because he had forsaken her, just like God. But the pattern was really amplified when she started her medium-ship because her subconscious feared that, now she was passing on messages from spirits, she would end up being judged and killed, as before. The weight was the suppressed fear, and also the suppressed anger because of again helping others. And all for her not being taken care of, because her subconscious believed she had been abandoned by God. Violet, like many other similar cases I have dealt with, would overtly play-up the messages, using names of her spirit guides or attributing them to someone else. Part of Violet's daily confrontation ended up being able to own the messages she actually picked up on.

In a nutshell, many psychic and psychic mediums decide to work in that field as a result of deep-rooted emotional trauma. They don't understand the subconscious and they start trying to 'read' for others before they have done the work on themselves. This allows the likes of Derren Brown to deride psychics, and rightly so. Like any profession there are experts and cowboys and everything in between. It is just so frustrating when you hear psychics telling people what they want to hear, just to gain approval, or controlling people by scaring them into thinking they need to ask the psychic (keep coming back) or giving them vague, wishy-washy readings. They cease to be a clear channel because of all their own emotional turmoil getting in the way.

I have obviously concentrated on the psychic and healing professions with relevance to a pattern of weight issues, but believe me, I have seen many a slim psychic charlatan too. It's just that their emotional blocks have been patterned to drugs, alcohol, or obsessive behaviours instead of food and weight. The upshot of this chapter is being able to understand 'spiritual ego', the pattern of taking responsibility for everyone else before taking responsibility for yourself; recognising if, and where, your destructive pattern means you are exhausting yourself by trying to rescue, heal and help the world rather than nurturing yourself.

## Exercise

Sit quietly in a room for at least half an hour doing absolutely nothing, with no distractions. After you have managed that, write down all the thoughts that popped into your head, or the amount of times you almost got up because you thought of someone you had to ring, or something you had to do, etc.

# 26

## THE SLIMMING ART OF SILENCE

All the chapters in this book of topics and exercises are interconnected. The relevance of understanding 'spiritual ego' in the previous chapter leads to an often maligned and forgotten art in today's society – silence and being still.

If you are used to doing everything for everyone else, it is a real challenge to allow yourself to sit quietly. Remember the subconscious is screaming at you from the inside to get busy making yourself invaluable to others, or busy distracting yourself. This is because when we sit quietly our emotions rise to the surface. They are always trying to rise to the surface, but usually they get squashed back down again with food or partially ignored by our keeping busy with other people or ourselves. Previously it may have been very difficult to sit quietly without occupying yourself, your mind or your body or misdirecting yourself with the trials and tribulations of others. The thing is that 'silence', used properly, can benefit you on many levels. The difference between sitting quietly and consciously focusing on chewing the food you are eating, for example, aids for a much smoother digestion than scoffing down while at your desk surfing the internet. When we are eating, we are actually consuming. Consuming in terms of what other information we are digesting along with our food as well!

Picture this. You are sitting quietly somewhere gazing out at some trees and a river, focusing on chewing your chicken sandwich, compared to watching the evening news while you are unconsciously chewing your chicken sandwich. You are also absorbing the fearful imagery of a tragic earthquake in China, listening to the injured cries and seeing death and destruction. Those images will literally tumble in with your meal, creating a masticated mash of food and negativity, and also the chemotional cocktail we discussed earlier, as your own subconscious responds to releasing negative emotion hormones.

> '*Not merely an absence of noise, Real Silence begins when a reasonable being withdraws from the noise in order to find peace and order in his inner sanctuary.*'
>
> Peter Minard

Being able to sit still and quietly with silence is a test for your progress in *The Weigh Forward*, because even the very nature of modern life means we have continual access to distraction. Mobile phones, the internet and chat forums, twenty-four-hour satellite television and supermarkets all have conspired to make it easier to distract ourselves, to suppress emotion and disconnect from the reality of what is actually going on with your subconscious.

Silence often becomes associated with forms of meditation and, by attaching such a label, it will already be pressing buttons with the subconscious. If there have been any abandonment issues, the subconscious understands meditation as connecting to God, so will sabotage an effort to meditate. Mediation itself is made by many other so-called 'spiritual people' convoluted and complicated. Whereas, all you need to do is sit quietly and give your conscious mind a focus while you allow the silence to resonate throughout your subconscious and soul.

An easy focus can be simply to look softly at a candle flame, and nothing else. Your mind will wander and random thoughts and emotional attachments surface, and as soon as you realise your mind has wandered from the candle flame, you return your conscious attention to it.

You could also just say a positive affirmation slowly and continually in your mind: 'I am safe, secure and protected by my light at all times.' Again, your mind will surface thoughts and emotions but all you have to do is keep returning to your affirmation. Both examples are an easy powerful way to sit in silence and allow your subconscious to de-junk – more importantly, you will wonder what all the fuss was about. All that business and distraction, for what? Subconscious fears, fears that are not real and, once faced, made to seem very small indeed. Many people over the years have attached different apt acronyms to the word 'fear'. As I have explained earlier, it is something we are fed daily to keep us stuck.

F E A R – False Evidence Appearing Real.

# 27
## FAT AND THE FOOD INDUSTRY

I told you at the start of this book that I wouldn't be spending time outlining the history of diets and the many different guises so-called 'food plans' have. For me it's a waste of valuable space to regurgitate researchable and outdated information. What is important is to recognise the key to weight loss lies in understanding and clearing emotional blocks by working on a subconscious level, before understanding the current chemical makeup of today's food industry.

It is embarrassing to look at diets which still, to this day, focus your attention on fats, carbohydrates and proteins and not on the most dramatic influences when it comes to food – chemicals.

Now is the time in this book to look at food and find a way for you to settle into a balanced approach to eating - once and for all. The way to do that is to de-link, as I have explained, from the perception of diets.

Diets make you fat by:

- Creating negative attitudes to foods
- Creating patterns of deprivation with foods
- Associating yourself with everyone else's failures by joining the group consciousness of diets
- Creating a dependency outside of yourself and placing your so-called success

or failure in the hands of slimming organisations (they make their money by your reliance on them)

- Creating duality with food and eating
- Trying to override your emotional subconscious blocks

But diets also make you fat by misdirecting you about food and deliberately not educating you on the natural processes of the body. One of the biggest abominations to have entered our food chain in the last twenty years is chemicals and genetically modified food. There has been a deliberate and sinister movement by the huge pharmaceutical industries to control our food and, by consequence, the population.

I will return to the chemical manipulation of our food in a moment, but to backtrack slightly, we have to change our thinking on how we perceive food. What do I mean by that? Well, we are conditioned to think in terms of imagery and groupings of food – breads, cereals, vegetables, fruits, meat, dairy, etc. The problem is the bread our grandparents ate is unrecognisable to the majority of bread we eat today; easily digestible natural ingredients have been replaced with industrialised processes that use artificial emulsifiers, preservatives and enzymes – and that's just for starters. The majority of cereals today are industrially processed using hydrogenated oils, additives, synthetic vitamins and an extrusion of grains (where the grain is treated with high heat and pressure, killing off any nutritional value). The milk we buy now is in many cases taken from cattle fed concoctions of antibiotics and human growth hormones. The same goes for the majority of our commercially farmed meat. Many vegetables and fruits, unless stringently organic, have been bathed in chemicals from seed to shop floor. This means that any argument for following certain meal protocols of our ancestors or neighbouring countries is missing the point. Your food has probably been 'Frankensteined' anyway. There is also the chemical interference of our plasticised food packaging, as well as the other industrialised processes, like ultra-heat treating (which kills any goodness in that food) or our own cooking habits, such as microwaving, which does the same.

## Fat And The Frankensteining Of Food

By around 1997, GM ingredients appeared in over 65 per cent of all processed food in the United States. A result of a single US Supreme Court ruling that allowed, for the first time, the patenting of life forms for commercialisation. You can only imagine the huge financial players who pounced on this ruling, and those involved with international stock exchanges who recognised the mergers of the massive players in the agrochemical business around this time.

There are obviously important ramifications on an environmental, ethical, philosophical and spiritual level, but with relevance to *The Weigh Forward*, it is an excellent reference point for comparing the rise in obesity levels and major diseases such as cancer in the last fifteen years. Part of this leap in genetic manipulation is also tied in with Hybridisation and Genetically Modified Organisms. Recombient DNA is a form of artificial DNA that is created by combining two or more sequences which would not normally occur together (tomatoes being spliced with fish genes is one of a million examples).

In terms of GM, it is created through the introduction of relevant DNA to an existing organismal DNA, such as the plasmids of bacteria, to code for or alter different traits for a specific purpose, such as antibiotic resistance. It differs from genetic recombination in that it does not occur through natural processes within the cell, but is engineered. A recombinant protein is a protein that is derived from recombinant DNA. The health ramifications of this cellular manipulation is already manifesting in higher incidences of skin allergy, defects, cancer, infertility, super viruses, interior toxins and an all round general lowering of nutritional value.

In the US population, the incidence of low birth-weight babies, infertility and infant mortality are all escalating. As a result, the American Academy of Environmental Medicine (AAEM) called on: 'Physicians to educate their patients, the medical community, and the public to avoid GM foods when possible and provide educational materials concerning GM foods and health risks.'

They called for a moratorium on GM foods, forming long-term independent studies, and adequate and honest labelling on food products. AAEM's position paper stated: 'Several animal studies indicate serious health risks associated with GM food,' including infertility, immune problems, accelerated aging, insulin regulation and changes in major organs and the gastrointestinal system. They concluded:

> *'There is more than a casual association between GM foods and adverse health effects. There is causation, as defined by recognised scientific criteria. The strength of association and consistency between GM foods and disease is confirmed in several animal studies.'*

When I intuitively talk of 'chemotional cocktails', it is interesting to note that the twentieth-century saw an incremental lowering of infectious disease rates, especially where a single bacteria was overcome by an antibiotic, but a simultaneous rise in systemic, whole body or immune system breakdowns.

The epidemic of cancer is a major example and is affected by the overall polluted state of our environment, including in the pollution of the air, water and food we take in. The real impact cannot be revealed by experiments which look at just a few controlled factors or chemical isolates. Rather, all of nature is a testing ground.

A few years ago, scientists were startled that combining chemical food additives with chemical cocktails caused many times more toxic effects than the sum of the individual chemicals. More startling was the fact that some chemicals were thought to be harm-less by themselves, but not in such combinations.

For example, two simple chemicals found in soft drinks – ascorbic acid and sodium benzoate – together form benzene, an immensely potent carcinogen. Similarly, there are entirely new ways of rearranging the natural order with genetic mutations. Similar non-traceable influences can likewise cause cancer. We definitively know X-rays and chemicals cause genetic mutations, and mutagenic changes are behind many higher cancer rates as are the complications which arise when cells duplicate out of control. In the USA in 1900, cancer affected only about one out of eleven individuals. It now affects one out of two men and one out of three women in their lifetime. Cancer mortality rates rose relentlessly throughout the twentieth-century to more than triple, overall.

## Obesogens

On a physical level it should be becoming more obvious that our food is now inexorably linked to chemicals. In my chapter on chemotional cocktails, you are not what you eat; you are what you emote. The chemotional cocktail, though, is your emotion-releasing hormones mixing with the chemicals that are now prevalent in our food group.

Bruce Blumberg at the University of California coined the phrase 'Obesogens'. Obesogens may be functionally defined as chemicals that inappropriately alter lipid homeostasis and fat storage, change metabolic set points, disrupt energy balance or modify the regulation of appetite and satiety to promote fat accumulation and obesity.

There are many proposed mechanisms through which Obesogens can act, including alterations in the action of metabolic sensors; dysregulation of sex steroid synthesis, action or breakdown; changes in the central integration of energy balance including the regulation of appetite and satiety; and reprogramming metabolic set points. Some of these proposed pathways include inappropriate modulation of nuclear receptor function; therefore, Obesogens are classified as endocrine disrupting chemicals.

Several examples of known Obesogens include tributyltin, bisphenol A, diethylhexyphthalate, and perfluorooctanoate. Emerging evidence from laboratories around the world suggests that other chemicals will be confirmed as Obesogens in the near future.

Don't worry if it all sounds like chemical-speak and your eyes are glazing over. Keeping it very simple - there has been a huge influx of chemicals into our food and these have been reacting with our own changing emotional make-up to create destructive chemotional cocktails which are contributing to obesity.

Despite deliberate, sinister machinations by huge pharmaceutical industries to control our food, many people still naively think that certain chemicals entering our food group have just been an unfortunate consequence of having to make our food production more efficient to feed a burgeoning population – it's poppycock!

What is important to recognise is that your food is being chemically manipulated – the facts are there for you to research as deeply as you feel comfortable with – and, as a result, having cleared your emotional blocks you can make food choices that are nothing to do with diets.

Remember your thoughts and emotional balance are the most powerful tools available to you. More natural choices of food are easier to come to from a place of positive choice rather than one of conditioned fear.

## Medical Misconceptions

For far too long we have been taught to kowtow to the supposedly esteemed wisdom of doctors in general and the almost 'godlike' status society holds them in. Well, not this author, that's for sure! History has proved many a medical procedure suspect from the early days of bloodletting to performing lobotomies. While mistaken beliefs in many fields of knowledge can impair or imperil individuals, the calculus of the danger represented by erroneous medical concepts can be especially evident. Prescribing an ineffective treatment, for example, can be a death sentence to a patient with a serious disorder. Some treatments that were once widely accepted, in fact, are now known to be toxic even to otherwise healthy individuals. Nonetheless, detecting and rooting out such errors have frequently proved to be an extraordinarily arduous and prolonged task. The upshot is that the current modus operandi of the medical profession is 'if we can't drug it out we will cut it out' – a blatant disregard for the emotional and subconscious health of the patient. (There are many factors that have brought us to this place and a philosophical essay on the medical industry and an exposé of its culture of treating the symptom and not the cause is a book in itself.)

With weight loss, we now have surgery centred on bariatric procedures. Another blatant example of riding roughshod over the subconscious and emotional back story of a patient to bypass, remove, cut, squeeze, sheath or override the synergy of a patient's physical, mental and emotional body.

Bariatric surgery (otherwise known as weight loss surgery) is performed on people who are dangerously overweight. This is usually done by reducing the size of the stomach with an implanted medical device such as a gastric band or through the removal of a portion of the stomach (sleeve gastrectomy or biliopancreatic diversion with duodenal switch) or by re-secting and re-routing the small intestines to a small stomach pouch (gastric bypass surgery). I have seen clients who have had these procedures and witnessed first-hand the trauma of trying to override the subconscious and suppress the manifestation of emotional discordance within the body. But you can't override the subconscious and the emotional discordance. The resulting hormones and chemotional cocktails have to go somewhere. This suppressed anger and self-punishment accelerates emotional discordance in the liver and the gallbladder (seat of anger), which is why (in my understanding) gallstones are a common complication of any bariatric surgery. And – can you believe it – surgeons often remove the gallbladder as a preventative measure!

This year the papers were again full of the story of another overweight lady who died after gastric surgery – Sharon Mevsimler (who died in July 2010). As usual the papers focused on her having a massive birthday cake three months before she died and relatives sneaking junk food into the hospital. There was no delving deeper into Sharon's subconscious and the power of her suppressed emotions. She was quoted as saying the gastric band was stopping her scoffing the food she craved. She regretted having the band fitted and thought it was the easiest way to lose weight.

Reading between the lines, Sharon had put on weight after 'comfort eating' when she had post-natal depression. Again, the usual broad brushstrokes by using generalisations like 'comfort food' and 'depression'.

Sharon's death followed that of Renee Williams, who died twelve days after her gastric bypass operation in December 2007. Despite traumatic emotional events such as getting pregnant at a young age and in later life being knocked down by a drunken driver, all the news focused on was her voracious appetite. Her thirteen-year-old daughter, Mirina, seems to be the only wise one among them: 'I kept telling her she was eating her emotions.'

These medical procedures and interventions are now even being proved to be increasing the likelihood of death in patients. It took a while for any clinical studies to be carried out, but researchers led by Dr. Lewis H. Kuller at the Department of Epidemiology, University of Pittsburgh, compiled data on every bariatric surgery done in Pennsylvania on residents during the decade from 1995 through 2004, and compared them with mortality data. Actual deaths are the most accurate figures to measure outcomes and the least amenable to statistical manipulation.

There were 16,683 bariatric surgeries done in Pennsylvania during that decade: 82.3 per cent on women and 17.7 per cent on men. The average age of the patients was forty-eight (median age forty-nine). Most of the deaths (82.7 per cent) occurred in patients who'd been patients of the hospitals performing most of the surgeries (90 per cent), adding strength to this evaluation being of the procedures themselves, not surgical centres or surgeons. During the first thirty days, about 1 per cent of all of the bariatric patients had died. The highest post-op deaths were among those over 55, with those over 65 having more than a three-fold increased risk. Thereafter, among the average age patients, annual death rates were about 1.31 per cent for the women and 4.09 per cent for the men.

Looking at the cumulative deaths according to the time after surgery, they found that nearly 3 per cent had died after the first year and 6.4 per cent of the patients were dead by the end of the fourth year following their surgeries. They also looked at long-term risks, reporting:

> *We also estimated the long-term mortality for individuals who had undergone surgery many years ago. For the 1995 cohort who had at least 9 years of follow-up, 13.0% had died. From the 1996 cohort with 8 years of follow-up, 15.8% had died, and from the 1997 cohort with 7 years of follow-up, 10.5% had died. For the 1998-1999 cohorts with 5 to 6 years of follow-up, the total mortality was 7.0% to 2004.'*

Statistics may be confusing or seemingly innocuous but, if we put them into context, we can look at the death rates among Americans of the same average age and weight of the bariatric patients for comparison. (Ignore, for a moment, the popular observation made by obesity organisations that if so many overweight people were dropping dead every four years, there would be no overweight people left.) The US National Centre for Health Statistics of the Centres for Disease Control and Prevention Data reports that the overall death rate among Americans of the same age is 0.352 per cent — for men it is 0.44 per cent while for women this age it's 0.26 per cent. These are miniscule compared to the numbers dying after bariatric surgery.

I have chosen to highlight the worrying inadequacies of surgical procedures, because I have devoted these pages to the pharmaceutical industries and the increase of destructive chemicals in our food groups. The slimming pills either bought off the shelf or prescribed by doctors are making pharmaceutical companies billions of pounds, with very little effect in achieving long-term weight loss – the market is rife with solutions which suppress the waves of appetite in the brain, or else restrict the gut capacity for digesting food. The side effects of drugs that interfere with the activity of the brain may result in raised blood pressure, chest pain, fever, hair loss, de-pression, impotence, heart damage and much more. Likewise, the side effects of a gut-related drug like Xenical, licensed for long-term use, are diarrhoea, unexpected faecal discharge and oily stools, if not followed up with a low-fat diet plan.

All in all, they are sold with complete disregard for the subconscious and emotional health of the client, rife with destructive side effects and condition the belief system of people to look towards a quick fix – regardless of the suffering – instead of addressing the real reasons behind weight gain.

# 28

## BULIMIA AND ANOREXIA: THE EMOTIONAL CAUSES

This is an apt stage to cover the emotional cause of bulimia and anorexia, considering many of the slimming pills and products mentioned in the previous chapter are taken by people with eating disorders, along with purging products like laxatives.

## Bulimia

*Bulimia Nervosa* is an eating disorder characterised by recurrent binge eating, followed by compensatory behaviours. The most common form is defensive vomiting, sometimes called 'purging'; fasting, the use of laxatives, enemas, diuretics, and over-exercising are also common. On an emotional level people who suffer from bulimia are literally finding it hard to digest life, meaning that they are going through a stage of low self-worth and are not feeling safe in the world. It is common in girls around puberty (although increasing numbers of boys are suffering from it too) because, on an energetic level, a child de-links from their mother at that time and is trying to find their place in the world. If because of insecurity, low self-worth or as a result of some form of trauma or abuse the surfacing emotions are too painful, the person will subconsciously be drawn to stuffing food in (bing-ing), to literally enmesh with the painful emotions, then purge that food and the emotions with it. This is obviously only a short-lived emotional reprieve, and despite the negative health effects of binging and purging (chronic gastric reflux after eating, dehydration and hypokalemia caused by frequent vomiting, electrolyte imbalance, which can lead to cardiac arrhythmia, cardiac arrest, gastroparesis or delayed emptying constipation, infertility and peptic ulcers) the negative emotions will quickly surface again.

Certain life-changing events like passing exams, leaving school, getting a good job, having a child, getting married, can temporarily make the subconscious feel safe again and reassure it with a more secure and valid place in the world (by being employed, married, a mother), although it is common for the habit of binging and purging to resurface if the status quo is rocked once more, which is why it is again so important to deal with the subconscious and root emotional block.

## Anorexia

*Anorexia Nervosa* is an eating disorder characterised by refusal to maintain a healthy body weight, and an obsessive fear of gaining weight due to a distorted self-image, which may be maintained by various cognitive biases that alter how the affected individual evaluates and thinks about their body, food and eating. It is a serious mental / emotional illness with a high incidence of comorbidity and also the highest mortality rate of any psychiatric disorder. (Again medical professionals call it a psychiatric disorder when it is an emotional disorder.) It is one of the hardest for the medical profession to treat because it is one of the illnesses where the absolute core block which we are all dealing with in our subconscious – self-worth – is at its most potent. In my understanding dealing with hundreds of clients with anorexia, the core subconscious emotional blocks always come down to self-hatred.

Whatever the emotional event – and it can be past life – the person has felt so abandoned and turned that abandonment into self-hatred that they are actually refusing to be taken care of by life. Although the focus is on the person not eating, and there is validity in using starvation because they feel it is the only area of their life where they can exercise control, there is the underlying issue of not feeling worthy of being fed, of being nourished and of being nurtured. On a self-worth level they have reached a nadir. Anorexia sufferers have to deal with their emotional blocks and their subconscious to move forward, which is why they prove such difficult cases for the medical and psychiatric professions.

Danielle had started starving herself aged eleven and continued well into her teens, ending up hospitalised at nineteen weighing just five and a half stone. She didn't respond to medical intervention and counselling didn't get to the bottom of her issues. With *The Weigh Forward* programme, I regressed Danielle as far back as the womb and her mother saying to her errant husband: 'I wish I didn't have this fuck inside me that will probably turn out a waster like you and I should have it aborted.' Danielle's subconscious had absorbed that hatred and although her father left before she was born and her mother brought her up with much love, Danielle's subconscious emotions of worthlessness were rampant. When she went through puberty, she put on a bit of puppy fat, and this is where all her patterning mixed together to begin her destructive behaviour. Danielle's mother hated fat people and was always making derogatory comments about them. Danielle subconsciously triggered her own mother's hatred towards her from when she was in the womb, associating it with body size and shape. She was subconsciously experiencing an energetic abandonment from her mother (as all children do in puberty) and her mother had also lied to Danielle as a child saying her father had run off with a skinny woman from work. You can see the subconscious working over time here, churning out strong emotions of self-hatred and associating them with weight and shape. What was fascinating for Danielle was that when she asked her mother about the incident in the womb, her mother was mortified that Danielle knew and thought she had secretly met up with her father, who had told her. Danielle was able to clear the core emotional block, change her pattern of self-punishment and associations with weight, and after breaking free from her anorexia, made contact with her father, feeling equipped to deal with life for the first time.

# 29

## NUTRITION FROM THE INSIDE OUT

There comes a point, once you have cleared your core emotional blocks and understood your sub-conscious patterns, when you will obviously bring your attention to food. There are countless diet books on the market and most of you will probably understand standard nutritional advice as well as the foodies writing the books. With all the books there will be common themes and also slightly quirky approaches. One thing is for sure, though; however much you have understood what the books have to offer, in the past you would have sabotaged sticking to any type of regime, because of the underlying subconscious reasons.

You will be surprised that after trying so many diets over the years you will now know deep down what types of food and eating habits feel right for you. Remember, now that you have been working with your subconscious you can work with intuitively feeling what nutrition you want to now follow. I say that because the most destructive aspect of any food intake is when we eat to suppress negative emotions. Having cleared the root of these emotions it is so much easier for you now to recognise when an old emotional knee-jerk is being triggered, by reassuring yourself that you know exactly where it stems from. It then becomes almost impossible to eat the amount of the chemically destructive food that you would have in the past. If you no longer eat to suppress negative emotions then you will automatically find it easier to achieve balance with your food choices, and subsequent digestion and as-similation of those choices. *The Weigh Forward* with your nutrition now is *chemotional* –

195

to reduce where possible the chemicals that you consume with your food and drink, and being mindful of your emotions each time that you do.

The major malaise of the last twenty years is fear. This is what inhibits your self-worth; this is your work with *The Weigh Forward* – from the inside out. Which means the most powerful work you have done is clearing destructive emotional blocks and re-validating yourself to not be driven by conscious or subconscious fear. I will say it again – your thoughts and emotions are the most powerful tools you have.

The understanding of food / chemicals and emotions follows on from your rejection of fear and not the other way around; the person who masters their thoughts and emotions will master their weight more effectively than the person who only masters their food. I have laboured this point because the information that follows with reference to your food and chemical intake is a complement to the work you do with your subconscious, and not the be-all and end-all.

## Chemotional Understanding

The rest of this chapter will continue with the theme of weight loss from the inside out, by explaining the chemical differences of food and drink which may be the same in name and completely different in nature, and the emotional associations with different organs of our bodies. For example, a chicken fed on fresh grain and seed pickings from organic earth while happily pecking around a farmer's land, will have a completely different chemical make-up compared to a chicken that is battery farmed and fed dead meat offal and pumped full of antibiotics and growth hormones, living in fear, and in pain. In short, destructive chemotional cocktails include poisoned water, polluted food, poisoned air, lack of nutrients, movement, sunshine, oxygen and negative fear-based thoughts, which are the cause of disease within the body and toxaemia, the presence of toxins in the blood. Let's deal with these factors first.

## Water

Water is crucial to our health and our life-force; everyone understands this on some level yet forgets the subtleties of this importance. The body is around 60 per cent water, water that is vital for helping us digest our food, transport waste and control our body temperature through our blood. If we look at these percentages of water within our body, though, our blood is actually 83 per cent water, the brain 70 per cent and, tellingly, body fat is only 10 per cent compared to lean muscle tissue, which is 75 per cent. In essence, overweight people have less than slimmer people. Even on a basic physiological level that means holding on to weight is limiting digestion and the transport of waste materials out of the body. On a physical level, we have reached a time in our lives and a cultural zeitgeist where we now have to pay attention to the source and quality of our water. Whether you understand the profusion of chemicals that have been added to our water supply, or the demands of an ever increasing population or even the way global warming is affecting its quality, it is a valid place to start.

On an emotional level, in Chapter 18 I talked about energy vibration and our thoughts and emotions affecting our reality. Considering that everything is vibrating matter, this means our rooms, furniture and clothes can carry our negative programming. Even more powerfully this applies to our food and water. Our thoughts, feelings, voice vibration and environment all affect our water, and not just before we drink it but also during the time it is assimilated in our bodies.

In the early nineties, I used to fill a litre bottle of water from my same filtered source and give it to clients to carry with them for three days. I then used to read the person intuitively by divining the water. For me, as an intuitive, it was an excellent medium for seeing how the client's emotional world of fears, doubts, worries, frustrations and dreams, goals and aspirations had imprinted on the water. If you are working on an intuitive level you can divine with anything because it is just a tool for your channelled connection to flow through. I just chose water because even at that early stage I recognised how it began to vibrate to the person's energy.

In recent times Dr Massaru Emoto has done some fascinating studies, including research-ing water and its connection to thoughts and consciousness (*The Hidden Messages in Water*), in which he demonstrates the effects of intentions, emotions and music on crystalline micro-clusters, visible in frozen water crystals.

Once you have organised the most balanced water that suits you on a chemical level, it is also important to then 're-energise' your water on an emotional level before drinking it. Distilled and bottled water which has been on shelves or in pipes for any length of time can become stagnant. To bring it back to life you can shake it for fifteen seconds, use a water vortex device or oxygen drops. To revitalise the energy of their water my clients have used different approaches like sticking labels on their water with positive messages (love, health), singing, speaking or playing healing music over it. They follow this up (as with all their food and water intake) by ensuring they are eating and drinking with positive thoughts and emotions.

Dehydration is one of the major causes of stress, and emotional discordance can also cause de-hydration. Polluted air and the bombardment of electro-magnetic frequencies (televisions, comput-ers, travel, flying, hairdryers, vaccinations and drugs, for example) can all cause dehydration. With that in mind, yes, water helps rehydrate, but addressing the other forms of dehydrators mentioned is also important.

Finally, when I talk about water, I mean *water*. So many people confuse drinking with hy-dration; apart from diluted fruit juice and herbal teas all other drinks are dehydrators to varying degrees or another.

## Food

I covered much of the chemical abuses of our food industry in Chapter 26, but remember, when retraining your body through nutrition after clearing your emotional blocks, a chemo-tional understanding is *The Weigh Forward*.

Our modern food conundrum is that a burger and chips could be less stressful on the body than a plate of vegetables and steamed salmon, if, and there is an 'if', you *think chemotional*. If you steamed a factory farmed salmon you would be eating a chemical mish-mash. Industrial salmon operations use a number of other chemicals to raise marketable fish. All of these pose known risks to human health. These substances include oxytetracycline, an antibiotic that may lead to antibiotic resistance. Like the controversial use of antibiotics by the poultry and livestock industries, these salmon farms must prevent fish from infecting one another with diseases. Because of the high prevalence of drugs on salmon farms, you may ingest untold amounts of antibiotics.

Industrial salmon farms also use unnatural food to feed the fish and artificial colour to make farmed fish — whose flesh is typically greyish white — appear a more appetising 'salmon' pink. One of the most commonly used dyes, Canthaxanthin, has been linked to human eye defects and retinal damage. If you then eat vegetables with it that have been dowsed in pesticides and chemically packaged, then the pollutants entering your body will outweigh a standard nutritionist's advice of avoiding burger and chips, even though your burger and chips may be organic.

The point of the example is to start thinking of food in terms of eating the least chemically bastardised meals, with the backing of the most positive thoughts and emotions – that is, optimising *chemotional digestion*.

## Chemotional Digestion

Most people consider the effects of food and the processes of food to begin once you have actually eaten it, which is actually not true. For optimum chemotional digestion it begins with your food choices, in terms of reduced chemical content and your ability to eat mindfully with positive emotions and the resultant positive hormonal influx that will add to the chemical mix.

Before a bite of food is even taken it is good to smell your food, which will trigger the mouth to water. This is important as saliva contains amylase, which helps to start breaking down carbohydrates in the mouth. Chew your food and allow the amylase to help the digestion process. It goes without saying that harmonious thoughts and feelings will help. Any angry or fearful thoughts will inhibit amylase and destructively mix with it too, creating discordance with digestion before the food has even left your mouth.

The food then moves to the stomach where pepsin and hydrochloric acid begin to break down proteins. The next stage is the small intestines – where pancreatic juice from the pancreas and bile from the liver alkalise the mix and breaks down fats, carbohydrates, sugars and proteins. This is where the chemicals in your food (antibiotic residues, artificial additives, genetically modified foodstuffs) get thrown into the mix along with the hormones released depending on how you are feeling.

So it's either a full on chemical sludge enveloping your usual digestion of processed food chemicals and angry and fearful hormones or a purer chemical mix of the natural enzymes breaking down your natural food with harmonious chemical hormones released from a place of calm. Imagine this daily chemical process going on in your body. Chemotional distress many times a day will only lead to weight and health complications; vital health and energy will emerge from a positive chemotional mix. This is how important your chemotional intelligence is. Not only is every meal time an opportunity for the uneducated and lazy to exacerbate ill health, but these days so is drink time, with most drinks from the 'bisphenol A' can-lined poison of soft drinks to the processed and genetically modified coffee bean, multiplying the amount of daily chemotional distress the body is subjected to. Forget your diets and slimming programmes, and embrace chemotional intelligence.

It is acceptable to say that stress reduces your ability for nutrient absorption, increasing nutrient excretion – the urinary loss of calcium, magnesium, potassium, zinc, chromium, selenium and various micro-minerals. Stress will also raise LDL levels (blood pressure), blood pressure aggregation, which is a major risk in heart disease, salt retention, cortisol (associated with weight gain and premature aging) and also destroy the healthy bacteria in the gut, diminish your thermic efficiency and salivary secretions, to name but a few so-called stress responses. What is actually happening is the subconscious is controlling these chemical releases (stress responses) due to manufacturing certain conditions in the body to keep weight and body fat on as protection from suppressed emotions.

So chemotional intelligence is certainly weight loss from the inside out. By healing core emotional events from your past, you are creating healthier hormonal releases in the body and working with your subconscious to let go of stored weight and return to a state of balance.

Understanding your stress is your chemotional intelligence. Rather than fobbing yourself off with 'I'm stressed', the tools provided in *The Weigh Forward* programme enable you to say, for example:

> '*I am suppressing a lot of angry thoughts because of the pressure I am putting on myself to make my partner love me, because I am so fearful of being rejected, which stems all the way back to the vulnerability of my father leaving when I was a child.*'

# 30

## CHEMOTIONAL PATHWAYS

I talk about weight loss from the inside out, and *The Weigh Forward* has highlighted the core emotional block as the primary focus to clear, then re-pattern the thoughts and ability to deal with triggered emotions. On a cellular level the suppressed emotion will have created different reactions within the body and all the major organs. Carrying extra weight / body fat is the final tangible expression of a complex 'chemotional path' where different organs of our body will react to different emotions and trigger the release of different hormones, creating the chain of events that will result in holding on to weight as protection. This can be similarly explained by Hering's Law. Constantine Hering (1800-1880) observed that healing occurs in a consistent pattern. He described this pattern in the form of three basic laws that homeopaths can use to recognise that healing is occurring. This pattern has been recognised by acupuncturists for hundreds of years and is also used by practitioners of herbalism and other healing disciplines. According to the first of Hering's Laws,

> '...healing progresses from the deepest part of the organism – the mental and emotional levels and the vital organs – to the external parts, such as skin and extremities.'

Hering's second states that,

> '...*as healing progresses, symptoms appear and disappear in the reverse of their original chronological order of appearance. Homeopaths have consistently observed that their patients re-experience symptoms from past conditions.*'

According to Hering's third,

> '...*healing progresses from the upper to the lower parts of the body. For instance, a person is considered to be on the mend if the arthritic pain in his neck has decreased although he now has pain in his finger joints.*'

Hering's Law is a good example to help understand more clinically when I talk of weight loss from the inside out. It also helps explain that when someone embarks on a diet, as they initially lose weight they are releasing cellular memory and triggered emotions which led to the body holding on to weight in the first place. Hence those who try only on that physical level to lose weight will sabotage their efforts as they haven't acquired the tools of acknowledging, clearing and releasing the suppressed emotions and traumas that surface, as the reverse process (weight loss) takes place. They retrace the journey that led to the weight gain.

A journey is probably a good analogy to use when looking to understand your weight issues. At some point in your life you came to a metaphorical crossroads and, for example, followed the road that included father abandonment, destructive male relationships and an increase in weight or fluctuations at the crucial times of emotional suppression.

In following *The Weigh Forward* we make the journey back to the crossroads easier because we initially go straight back and clear that emotional trauma first, so that when you are healing (letting go of weight) you have the tools to release the emotional triggers and suppressions. You are in essence then clearing all the way back to the crossroads, to be able to take the other road from a place of wisdom, understanding and healing.

You may have lived many years on from your initial emotional trauma and repeated emotional shocks, which is why it is imperative to cleanse your *chemotional pathway*. The body's mechanism kicks in after psychological or emotional shock. The electrical activity that forms our thoughts flares up at times of emotion and energises the amygdala, a tiny nugget of tissue deep in the centre of the brain. This sets off a chain reaction that releases a powerful cocktail of chemicals into the blood stream. These include, on a general level, vasopressin to increase blood flow to the muscles, endorphins to block off pain and adrenaline and noradreneline to mobilise the body's glucose reserves. There will also be the unique hormonal release, depending on which specific emotion is triggered, added to the mix.

The problem with emotional conundrums of loss / rejection / abandonment is that we cannot successfully fight or run from it, and the feeling of danger that it poses is not likely to go away (without dealing with it on a subconscious healing level). The result is that a second mechanism – counter-shock – brings a new set of generalised hormones into play too.

In evolutionary terms, counter-shock is designed to help us withstand attack once we have failed to escape or fight it off. The hormones released include cortisol, which dampens down our inflammatory response to injury, thyroxine and glucocorticoid to conserve fuel reserves, growth hormone to repair damage to bones and anti-coagulants to stop us bleeding to death. These hormones may once have helped us to survive violent tussles with predators, but now counter-shock can quickly turn to exhaustion.

If the level of cortisol, the prime 'stress' hormone, is raised for a long period it undermines the immune system, amplified by the modern day chemical smorgasbord of food additives, antibiotics and growth hormones being added regularly to this destructive mix. People who live under constant emotional turmoil have been found to have reduced levels of NK (natural killer) cells, the blood corpuscles that seek out and destroy bacteria and viruses. Levels of T-Lymphocytes, the NK cells 'helpers', are also depleted along with immunoglobin, a protein that acts as an antibody. These changes make us less able to fight infection and more vulnerable to illness.

It is easy to see why working with our subconscious to clear emotional blocks is paramount to health; a healthy weight, a healthy body and a healthy mind. These suppressed emotions, dampened down regularly over a period of time, give way to a state of near-permanent anxiety, with familiar feelings of tension and dread and ultimately trigger phobias, panic attacks and insomnia, also bringing about physical changes like weight gain. An obvious example is the many women who have experienced how emotional discordance has wreaked havoc with their oestrogen and progesterone levels, sending their menstrual cycle awry.

## The Synergetic Link

Returning to weight loss from the inside out, I have thought long and hard about what part of my physical, emotional, mental and spiritual understanding to share in this book. The main area where all my clients have been most interested is understanding their synergetic link with their food, their bodies, their organs, their emotions, their thoughts and their environment. When I talk of a synergetic link, I use the term loosely from my own understanding.

Buckminster Fuller coined the term 'synergetics', defining it as the empirical study of systems in transformation, with an emphasis on total system behaviour unpredicted by the be-haviour of any isolated components, including humanity's role as both participant and observer. Since systems are identifiable at every scale from the quantum level to the cosmic, and humanity both articulates the behaviour of these systems and is composed of these systems, synergetics is a very broad discipline, and embraces a range of scientific and philosophical studies including tetrahedral and close-packed-sphere geometries, thermodynamics, chemistry, psychology, biochemistry, economics, philosophy and theology.

As I said, I use the term to refer to the concept of the output of a system not foreseen by the simple sum of the output of each system part; namely, our thoughts and emotions will affect our physiological processes, as will our environment and cellular coding of belief systems and thought processes when dealing with a seemingly simple equation of weight gain. Part of the synergetic link is the role of the different major organs of the body in having an emotional bias of what feelings they are triggered by and respond to, in greater or lesser proportion to each other. I have outlined below *The Weigh Forward*'s chemotional pathways of the major organs of your body.

## The Heart

On a physical level the heart is a hollow muscular pump responsible for propelling our blood around the body (circulatory system) and also in a shoot loop to the lungs and back again (pulmonary circulation). On an emotional level the heart is about how we handle the joy of life. Blood is literally our essence, rich and vibrant and healthy when we are embracing life and sitting in a place of genuine happiness. When we suffer emotional turmoil that literally squeezes the joy out of our life, the heart can suffer pain, as it draws to our attention our emotional discomfort.

On an energetic level our heart chakra is connected to the physical heart, the endocrine glands and also the thymus, because of its connection to the thymus gland. It is from here that the defence system of the body is activated. It is the gateway to the lungs which, when it becomes congested, can block the emotions of grief and sadness (lung ailments like asthma, bronchitis, fluid etc.) and the emotion of love.

It is through the heart that we connect and express ourselves. If we shut the heart because of a negative reaction to the emotional content of life, or by throwing energy up into the mind (intellectual protection) then the heart becomes troubled. The heart is connected to the solar plexus, the sacral centre and therefore the small intestines. Those that suffer M.E. or Candida etc. keep throwing energy / emotion from their heart into their head and so suffer lack of energy and infection in digestive areas. The heart is also connected to the breasts and the expression of love.

## The Liver

I described the liver's physical function earlier. It is a bit like a chemical factory, in charge of the whole metabolic process. Its function is in the storage and release of chemicals and minerals, processing sugars and fats, turning the fats into glucose etc. Liver function is very important to the nervous system because the brain function relies on glucose. The liver also neutralises intoxicating substances such as alcohol, drugs and toxic food. It secretes bile into the digestive system, which emulsifies oils and fats rendering them digestible.

The liver is often described as the general. The general is in charge of defence; it gives commands to the cells. In antiquity the liver was considered to be the seat of the mind and a liver blockage could give rise to grave emotional states. Depression is caused by blockages in the liver and emotions such as boredom, irritability, bitterness and frustration are all indicative of stones in the liver. The liver is responsible for the recycling of hormones, the formation of blood, and heat and energy production.

On an emotional level, the liver is the seat of anger – predominantly male anger. Our angry thoughts and suppressed emotions put a strain on the liver and can be one of the impetuses for developing the early onset of liver stones that travel to the gallbladder. Contrary to common belief, most gallstones are actually formed in the liver and very few in the gallbladder. Gallstones are one of the major reasons why people fall ill and have difficulty recuperating from an illness. There is rarely a disease in the body that does not start in the liver, and almost every patient with a chronic illness, such as diabetes, has an excessively large number of stones in their liver. Cleansing the liver is useful for a whole range of illnesses, from allergies to heart disease to chronic fatigue and menopausal difficulties.

It is the liver's job to detoxify blood on a physical level and it also detoxifies the emotions on an energy level. The liver clears anger but, as I mentioned above, especially in the Western world we use it as a storage space for negativity so it becomes stressed and eventually blocks. Most skin conditions are based in the liver, which range from small outbursts of anger (spots) to rage at the father (psoriasis). Managing the liver has to ultimately require a release of previously suppressed anger. Most planning within the body is done in the liver and the decision-making is done by the gallbladder. It is important to be assertive, and assertiveness is definitely part of the liver's function. By not being assertive you bottle up emotion and become angry. It is closely linked with the kidneys, because fear is sent across from the kidneys through the liver.

## The Spleen

On a physical level the spleen consists of two different tissue types — red pulp and white pulp — with two distinct functions. Red pulp, also called splenic pulp, consists of blood and reticular fibres. This portion of the human spleen helps to filter the blood, purging it of unwanted elements which contain red blood cells that have aged to the point of deterioration. White pulp, also called Malpighian bodies of the spleen or splenic lymphoid nodules, refers to small nodules within the spleen that are rich in lymphocytes and help to fight infection.

The spleen is a very important organ, and asplenia, a condition in which the spleen is not present either congenitally or due to removal in surgery, has been linked to an increased predisposition to certain infections. In traditional Chinese medicine, the spleen is said to influence one's temperament and willpower. On an emotional level, the spleen is reflective of your emotional relationship with your mother, your feelings about being a mother yourself and mothering everybody else. The spleen is the good mother so to speak, storing and distributing food to all the family. The Chinese understanding of the spleen also includes the pancreas. The health of the pancreas determines the quality and strength of its pancreatic enzymes and this determines how well nutrients are absorbed through the small intestines. Destructive emotions associated with the mother or strong female relationships in your life dampen down the effectiveness of the quality and strength of the enzymes that are released.

On an energetic level, the spleen chakra absorbs energy (chi) from the atmosphere, and also absorbs the energy from food and distributes it throughout the body. The spleen sends a lot of its energy to the sacral centre where it is stored before being distributed throughout the body. People who live on microwave meals are actually using their own energy to digest it as the food's living enzymes have been destroyed. Most of digestion in the stomach is done by bacteria, hence, as I mentioned in previous chapters, GM food is resistant to bacteria, so can't be broken down. The spleen chakra affects vitality because it passes chi into the blood, and can also affect the heart and immune system. It helps to produce the right balance of antibodies and assist in the elimination of living organisms like germs and viruses.

## The Kidneys

On a physical level the kidneys are sophisticated reprocessing machines. Every day, our kidneys process about two hundred quarts of blood to sift out about two quarts of waste products and extra water. The waste and extra water become urine, which flows to the bladder through tubes called ureters. The bladder stores urine until releasing it through urination.

Waste in the blood comes from the normal breakdown of active tissues, such as muscles, and from food. The body uses food for energy and self-repair. After the body has taken what it needs from food, waste is sent to the blood. If the kidneys did not remove them, these would build up in the blood and damage the body. The actual removal of waste occurs in tiny units inside the kidneys called nephrons. Each kidney has about a million nephrons. In the nephron, a glomerulus — which is a tiny blood vessel, or capillary — intertwines with a tiny urine-collecting tube called a tubule. The glomerulus acts as a filtering unit, or sieve, and keeps normal proteins and cells in the bloodstream, allowing extra fluid and waste to pass through. A complicated chemical exchange takes place, as waste materials and water leave the blood and enter the urinary system.

On an emotional level, the kidneys are the seats of fear. Dealing with fear is linked to the kidneys and governed by kidney energy. By working with your subconscious you can clear the core emotional blocks that are holding excessive fear and in re-patterning become much more balanced with handling day-to-day natural fears.

On an energetic level, the kidneys interconnect to the tan tien (hara or sacral centre), which connects us to all life, as in other humans, trees, plants etc. The kidneys are the foundation of the body. They contain the reserve or energy of life essence that is known as 'jing'. There is congenital jing that we are born with and relates to the constitution of our parents. There is also acquired jing, which can be obtained from food and herbs and which can fortify inherited jing. Substances that deplete jing include: pesticides in food, chlorinated or sodium fluoridated water, alcohol, drugs, unnecessary or excessive intake of vitamin and mineral supplements, coffee and tea, animal proteins, carbonated beverages, chocolate and sweets, tobacco and heavy metals. These substances also produce kidney stones, which can wreak havoc in our bodies and may manifest in a whole complex of symptoms, from hearing difficulties to infertility.

## The Lungs

On a physical level the lungs perform a multitude of vital functions every second of our lives. Breathing is the most essential of these functions. With each breath, the lungs take in oxygen and remove carbon dioxide. The air (oxygen) we breathe enters the lungs via the main windpipe (trachea), which branches into two main tubes supplying the right and left lung, respectively. The surface area of the lungs is huge -- larger than the surface of a person's skin. In fact, if all the airways and air sacs of a person's lungs were laid flat on the ground, they would more than cover a tennis court. Because the walls of these air sacs are one fiftieth the thickness of tissue paper and bathed with millions of tiny blood vessels called capillaries, there is an easy and efficient exchange of oxygen and carbon dioxide between the body and the environment. The lungs are also important in the body's defence against infection and other harmful environmental factors. While the nose is the first line of defence against inhaled harmful materials, the lungs provide the second line of defence. Inhaled particles (smoke, pollution) or infectious agents (bacteria, viruses) pass through the mouth or nose and lodge in the lungs.

On an emotional level, the lungs are linked to sorrow and grief; its outward expression being weeping and complaining. The lungs are always a way of releasing, letting go and detoxing the body. You can release immense amounts through the lungs. If you hold on to sorrow and grief, you have the potential to release it through the lungs. People hold on to a lot of tension and anxiety by shallow breathing. They do not allow the lungs to release everything they are holding. Coughs sometimes arise at times of excitement and change, or when the suppression overflows and subconsciously you are barking at the world, because of your sadness at injustices perceived to have been inflicted on you. People with weak lungs are confused by the experience of loss and suppress their sadness, never completely letting go.

On an energetic level, the lungs receive vital force from the air and mix it with the chi (energy) extracted from food. This combination of chi and nutrients is then distributed throughout the whole body. The skin and hair are also nourished and warmed by lung energy. The lung meridian is also strongly connected to the diaphragm. When you breathe more deeply, the diaphragm has to move more, which then massages the digestive system. This in turn helps in the production of bile, coming from the liver through the gallbladder, and which also encourages the excretion of pancreatic enzymes. So if you can go for a good walk following your meal, it forces your diaphragm to work that bit harder.

Lung energy is characterised by its ability to consolidate, gather together, maintain strength and unify against disease at every level, including cellular immunity. A person with sufficient lung energy is able to organise their life and hold on to their direction. How well we 'hold on' and 'let go' can be expressed in terms of emotional attachment. The large intestine is the complementary organ of the lung, and also has its function in releasing what is no longer needed. The release is on all levels; physical, emotional and spiritual. Virtually everyone with lung and colon problems has unresolved sadness that needs to be cleared.

## The Stomach

On an emotional level, any disharmony within the stomach and the spleen together is a result of 'mother issues'; old, repressed fears, hurts and angers to do with your own mother, and consequent negative emotions triggered by the broader term of mothering or strong females in your life. It is also the physical area where our fears and dread can be felt. Similarly to the example I gave about bulimia the stomach responds to how well you are literally digesting life. When you are at ease and feel comfortable with life, the stomach is in balance.

From our inception, we absorb food and rely on our mother to give us what we require. This is also so before our birth, when we are in the womb. The stomach meridian represents the mother, and the liver meridian, the father. (This is why it is beneficial for a mother and child when breastfeeding to alternate from one breast to the other, switching from the masculine yang energy to the feminine yin energy of the milk.)

On an energetic level, the stomach picks up on those emotions of fear and dread. The old saying 'I feel it in the pit of my stomach' is more apt than you can imagine. They may be literal fears of money, health and relationship, dreading having to confront bills, a nagging pain or the possibility of a relationship ending, or may be less tangible; the vague feeling of impending doom, which may not necessarily be accurate but a subconscious dramatisation of a problem that will need confronting.

## The Small Intestine

On a physical level, the small intestine receives partially digested food from the stomach and further aids digestion. It is one of the most active organs in the body. Many chemical reactions take place in the small intestine and there is an intense production of heat. It receives food processed by the stomach, bile from the gallbladder and pancreatic enzymes from the pancreas, taking what is beneficial for the body and filtering it through the bloodstream. The waste products get sent to the large intestine for final processing before elimination.

On an emotional level, the small intestine is closely linked to the heart and the heart is the controller of the mind. Our scattered thoughts, fears and other emotions are held in the small intestines, the organ intrinsically linked to our thoughts. It is why when people are detoxing through fasting or cleansing processes they will experience scattered thoughts, as all the toxins resurface along with negative thoughts and feelings from the past. I do highly recommend certain forms of cleansing but it amazes me how many therapists run fasting and detoxing programmes, yet pay little regard to the cellular surfacing of these old emotions. Old emotions tend to be held in the small intestine, so a calm and peaceful mind will come from a centred and clean intestine.

On an energetic level the small intestine is a yang organ, which means it's an expressive organ – it gives. However, if the small intestine does not receive what it needs in terms of nutrient-rich food, it creates imbalance in the body. Being so strongly linked to your thoughts, if you are mindful of your thoughts your digestion will be more balanced, and vice versa.

## The Large Intestine

On a physical level, the large intestine or more common moniker bowel or colon stores the waste derived from our food before it is expelled from our body. Receiving this waste material from the small intestine, it absorbs its fluid content, forming the remainder into faeces, which is excreted.

On an emotional level, the large intestine is actually to do with our past. People who hold on emotionally to the past and have a reluctance to letting go of old hurts, traumas and events will hold on to waste in their colon. These waste products can build up and actually be present for years. This was demonstrated by astronauts who ate a very cleansing pure diet in space and, when their waste products were tested on their return, content from foods they had not eaten since childhood were found including a toy one of the astronauts had swallowed as a kid. With the chemotional pathways of the colon, vitamins and minerals can be absorbed in the bowel but if the colon is blocked toxins are released back into the bloodstream which will hold the toxic memory of past hurts and feelings too.

On an energetic level, the colon is the harbourer of older, more stagnant emotions. People who have been extremely passive and refused to express themselves have these suppressed emotions not only stored in the liver, but the colon too. The liver, intestines and lungs are very much connected. They are yin organs which mean they attract and hold energy.

# 31

## CHEMOTIONAL EXERCISE

Given the widely available traditional diet and nutritional advice, I have chosen in *The Weigh Forward* to move on from the failing and limiting beliefs associated with their mantras, and concentrate on my understanding and development of the chemotional aspects of my work.

The same applies to exercise, and as a representative sportsman, black belt martial artist, physical education teacher and personal trainer I am probably more qualified than most when I say that people dealing with serious weight issues will subconsciously sabotage any efforts at exercise, regardless of intentions. Chemotional exercise is *The Weigh Forward*.

What I mean when I use the term is that once you have cleared your core emotional blocks, it is important to release the negative emotions associated with exercise. You can then choose a form of cardiovascular exercise and subsequent muscular strength endurance exercises, devoid of previous baggage from negative experiences or failures in the past.

It is dispiriting to watch certain television programmes, where you actually see the personal trainer getting angry with the client because they are not losing weight. Talk about ego and ignorance. The trainer takes it personally because in their understanding it is a simple task of just doing the exercise, then losing weight, whereas, for the client, their subconscious is screaming defiance at the vulnerable intrusion into its carefully laid plans of 'protection'.

So often you see the client get an injury or give up their training when the weight doesn't fall off. Chemotionally the person may be fighting repetitive destructive emotions from previous

exercise experiences, and the chemotional mix will be making their present experience negative too. Some examples of the negative attitudes to exercise:

- Always the last to be picked for school PE games.
- Being given exercise as punishment in class. (Old style PE teachers would misinterpret a body-conscious individual 'failing' at the physical tasks set as a disruptive pupil and send them off on a few laps of the playing fields, amplifying an already negative attitude to exercise)
- Any repressed emotions of embarrassment in the school showers or being told off for bringing a forged note to get out of games would surface on a return to exercise.
- A young girl starting her first period during exercise and the resulting emotional associations.
- Overly pushy parents making a child do a certain sport when they hated it. (Why would they choose to do exercise as an adult?)
- Accumulative adult failures of gym membership paid for and not used, of not achieving with a personal trainer etc.

The above are just a few examples but all of them can contribute to the subconscious associating exercise with embarrassment, failure, discomfort and pain. Those have to be cleared first, then a positive realignment to exercise made.

Again there is a plethora of actual exercise programmes on the market, from gym sessions to military copycat exercises in the local park. The most important factor is to settle with an exercise programme you can 'allow' yourself to do by working with your subconscious, and also do it 'mindfully' using, for example, your exercise as a perfect time to continuously recite your affirmations.

# 32

## CHEMOTIONAL CLEANSING AND EMOTIONAL CLEARING (YOUR GUIDED VISUALISATIONS EXPLAINED)

The purpose of your core emotional visualisation and subsequent clearing and healing is the building block, the main foundation stone of your success with *The Weigh Forward* programme. I wanted to explain the process I have developed and use to access your subconscious (and subsequently achieve clearing and healing) in this section. I have broken down your unique guided visualisation:

### Step 1 - Preparation
Undertaking any guided visualisation it is essential that you set aside at least half an hour when you know you won't be disturbed. Your environment is important in so much as you should choose somewhere at home where you feel safe and comfortable, where you can relax and be as free as possible from distractions. Having read earlier chapters you will understand that everything is energy and so called inanimate objects can hold the vibration of people's energy, especially charged emotional energy. With this in mind many people choose to dedicate a specific corner of a room somewhere in their house or even a whole room for a chair and meaningful spiritual items (crystals, icons, statues, flowers, etc.) which is solely used for relaxation, visualisation, meditation and contemplation. The higher vibration of this space will build over time and add to your experience. If you are choosing a chair in your kitchen

where you have screaming matches with your partner every night and crash, bang and wallop the utensils in frustration, anger and hopelessness, that area will certainly hold energy from those experiences.

I'm not saying you won't be able to complete your visualisations in the kitchen; it is more a case of setting out an intent and reverence to value what you are undertaking, the same way you could probably sit an exam in an outside car park with cars whizzing past, aeroplanes flying over-head and a brass band in the corner, but would feel more comfortable and 'on focus' in a silent exam hall. Discordant energy that is hanging around from destructive emotions and interactions is the vibrational equivalent of a poorly conducted brass band.

Most people feel comfortable sitting in a chair with their back straight and their eyes closed; others on a cushion on the floor or lying down on a bed or couch. As long as you are relaxed and comfort-able, that is fine. Begin by taking a few deep breaths, breathing right the way down into your tan tien, filling your lungs as much as possible, then sighing away your breath. Remember that deep breathing is a good way of expelling toxins and clearing the mind, so not only are you starting to relax more but already beginning a process of release. After some deep breaths I ask you in the visualisa-tion to see your 'weight box' in front of you. With your eyes closed, this is imagining a metaphorical container that you can use to hold all the negative energy you are retaining. The 'weight box' is any container you feel happy with to literally unload the 'weight off your mind'. When I guide you to put all feelings of negativity, all fears, any doubts, any worries and frustrations into your weight box, you are energetically dumping those negative energies into something outside of yourself. You may just hear my words and literally put the words fear, doubt etc. into the box, or you may surprise yourself with imagery of people, situations, and dark black gunk floating off your body, your mind and your aura into the box. All of that is fine; the most important part again is that you are stating the intent. The subconscious knows exactly what is being asked of it and the intent is enough. Some people initially doubt the effectiveness of their release into the 'weight box' because it isn't in high definition,

3D plasma glory. It doesn't work like that; many people work instantly with thought and their sub-conscious is ahead of the game – the intent is enough.

Referring back to energy again, you should always be responsible for your energy. Just like the argument-ridden kitchen, the black spot on a road of car accidents, the rough pub, the so-called haunted hotel, energy and especially fear lingers like an invisible clagging cloak of negativity. That is why I will guide you to see that once your weight box is full and you have released as much as you are comfortable letting go of into the box, you see it in your mind be taken away into the light where it can be transformed into positivity. Again people see all kinds of different scenarios for this, from the box being beamed into the heavens to 'light beings' picking it up and dissolving it into light.

I can only relate to you here from an intuitive level. I have watched people in gyms running on treadmills and claggy negative energy dropping off them that is invisible to the naked eye. The endorphins from the exercise create a different, more positive chemical reaction in the person and they release some of the stagnant chi from themselves. Other people in the gym are doing the same and walking around kicking clumps of this negativity around the place and invading other people's space with it. That may sound dramatic, but the same thing happens in hotel rooms; when a guest goes to sleep and their subconscious dreams, and releases fears in the night, this stagnant chi can hang around so the next night a different guest taps into the previous guest's energy. As I said, this is something for you to see if it resonates with you as a truth. I always clear the energy of a room when I stay in a hotel. There are many ways to do this that are simple and effective involving music, fresh air, or incense – I just visualise the negative chi being set on fire (in my mind), then send the residues into the light before filling the room with healing white light. Interestingly, a client of mine last year told me she stayed in a hotel in China that year, and they said they 'cleanse the rooms of negativity' after each guest – but then again the Chinese have always been more understanding and accepting of chi and employ Feng Shui across all levels of commerce from the local restaurant to the global banking group.

Once the 'weight box' has been sent into the light I then ask for you to see a golden and silver bubble of protective light coming around you and your space, and to see a colour enter that space. Again this is for you and your subconscious to feel safe and protected on an energetic level and, having released the 'weight off your mind' into your box, you are being proactive in drawing a positive colour (remember all colours carry a vibrational energy too, which is easily researchable in looking up information on colour therapy etc.) into your being.

All colours have positive aspects to them; the subconscious, though, has been more conditioned over time to associate red, black and grey more destructively because of conditioned imagery of blood, anger, seeing red and the so-called 'black horror of the night', and depressing grey days, so to reassure the subconscious if any of those colours come into your space, just see them dissipate and a brighter colour come in. You are then asked to breathe that colour deep into your being.

Having completed your preparation you are ready to begin your guided visualisation. I always ask to state a higher intent to the purpose of your visualisation asking the higher source that the journey you take is safe, secure and protected, and for your highest good and healing.

## Step 2 – Entering the Subconscious

Once you have breathed in as much of your positive colour as you can I ask you to go to your 'primary fat cell'. You will be drawn to an area of your body. Don't pre-empt this; again your subconscious knows exactly what it is doing and will draw your mind to that area of your body. I will then ask you to see a gateway open up in that fat cell with a beautiful light pathway leading upwards. You may see a door, gate or some elaborate entrance. Whatever gateway you see open up is fine; it is our entrance point into the subconscious and in your mind I ask for you to see yourself walking through that gateway, up the beautiful light pathway and into your meadow.

## Step 3 – The Invitation

Once you are in your meadow (which is a safe and secure place that your subconscious will feel comfortable in so don't be surprised if you recognise it), enliven your experience. Stimulate your senses and have fun settling yourself into the surroundings of your meadow. Feel the sunshine on your face, hear the light breeze rustling through the grass and see the colours of the different flowers.

Once you are comfortable we ask for the 'core block to healthy weight' to come into the meadow and a younger aspect of yourself will join you. (In essence this is an emotionally frozen aspect of you that responded to a certain trauma, misunderstanding or belief and has remained stuck in your subconscious at that point in time – *your core block*.) I ask for you to let the younger aspect of yourself to see that it is you and that you have come back to help them. You don't have to immerse yourself in the younger aspect's emotions. In your mind stand back slightly from them and ask them how they are feeling.

Unlike certain cognitive therapies and techniques you are not intellectualising how you may have felt at a younger age, or talking for the younger aspect of yourself. You are asking them how they feel, why they are feeling that way, what has happened, or how have they responded to something. It is important that, regardless of how you may have interpreted this over the years (if it is a remembered event), this is a fresh examination. You are asking the younger aspect and you are building a picture of what that younger aspect went through emotionally – how they felt a certain way and why. This part is your opportunity to enjoy working with your subconscious and taking part in your own healing. Take your time to ask questions of the younger aspect of yourself, to build up their story. There will be an abandonment and self-worth issue in there somewhere, so keep delving deeper with the questioning of your younger self until the story unfolds for you.

## Step 4 – The Catch-Up

Once you are 'happy' that you have understood the emotional associations of your younger self with their fear, doubt and worry, now is the time to show that younger aspect of yourself where you are now, currently in your life; to show them how far you have come since they experienced that trauma. You have to be strong here, regardless of how you may feel that you are still repeating fears from that younger age; you are now an adult who has adult choices in the world. You have a greater understanding of life and how it works. It is important that you show the younger aspect of yourself through your own eyes how their fears of abandonment and low self-worth are no longer the issue. You are committed to change and have moved on from that younger aspect of yourself. (This may entail you showing the younger aspect of yourself that your parents do / did love you, that you have attracted love in your life, that you have earned money, raised children, helped others, have had positive experiences.)

Whatever positives and understanding you demonstrate to the younger aspect of you, it is important you show them that you are in a position to no longer be controlled by that destructive emotion and now is the perfect time for the younger aspect to go into healing so you both can grow and move forward.

## Step 5 – The Healing

This part is the culmination of a core emotional release for you on many levels and also a subconscious reinstatement of your spiritual connection. Once you have shown the younger aspect of yourself how far you have moved forward and how ready you are to let go of the habit of the destructive emotion, ask the younger you if they are willing to go into healing. Spiritual light will take that aspect of you into healing (where other levels of healing on other realms can take place) before returning to you after a few days no longer stuck in the destructive emotional block, but a balanced part of your being.

I always suggest to clients to take this aspect of their healing on a level of understanding they feel comfortable with. Yes, this is a form of spiritual healing and in my understanding is an important aspect of the most powerful way I can help clients deal with a destructive past. It is funny how some people may think of prayer as second nature but block by intellectualising this form of spiritual healing. There are many ways to involve a higher consciousness to assist us both with specific understanding and intent, and also impassioned pleas when life is chucking difficult times at us. Either way over the years it is about what works; those that choose to always look to remain ignorant and doubt other levels of healing can remain in their narrow-minded worlds, but one thing is for sure they aren't handling life very well, and sooner or later they usually end up in the chair asking for help.

## Step 6 – Cellular Release

Once the younger aspect of you has been taken into the spiritual light for healing I then ask you to feel where that destructive emotional block has been held physically within your body. Your mind will be drawn to an area of your body. You can then ask for the spiritual light to take all the negativity away from this area of your body and into the light to be transmuted into positivity. Be aware of what area this is as you can visualise your body filling with positive healing light every day as you say your affirmations and re-pattern your subconscious.

## Step 7 – The Residues

I then ask for you to see the spiritual light come down and form a bridge into healing. This allows the subconscious to feel comfortable to then release 'all aspects of you that have experienced the same destructive emotions over the years'. If, for example, your core block was a six-year-old you feeling that if she had been 'better behaved' her dad wouldn't have left, you can then ask for all aspects of you repeating the same destructive emotions to go over the bridge into healing. It may mean you see in your mind thousands of aspects of you come in like a crowd of people at all ages of your life right up to the present day; they can come in and go over the bridge into healing. They are just repeats of the pattern, times when you may have suppressed anger / feared male abandonment / sacrificed your own wishes to be compliant etc. Once all the aspects of you have gone over the bridge into healing you are then ready for the wash through.

## Step 8 – The Wash Through

The subconscious likes completion, and at this stage I ask you to see a positive light colour come into the scene and wash through it, so the whole scene disintegrates and disappears, bringing your attention back to the meadow where we re-affirm to the subconscious: 'There is no longer any destructive block to hold me back and limit my path to letting go of weight.' Knowing the healing that has taken place during your visualisation will transmute itself into positivity and resonate throughout every single cell of your being, you then 'ground' yourself again by feeling the surroundings of your meadow ready for the penultimate stage.

## Step 9 – Reconnection and Re-Affirmation

At this point (post-healing) it is a perfect time to allow your subconscious to experience (remember to you it is a visualisation, to the subconscious it is reality) your direct connection to the highest source. You are asked at this stage of the visualisation to picture in your mind your connection to the highest source as a light shining down and through you, and also become aware that this highest source is within you. I then ask you to immerse yourself in that imagining for a few minutes while you silently repeat a core affirmation ('I am safe, secure and protected by my light at all times') so the subconscious can begin the rebuilding of your self-worth and understanding that you can never be abandoned because you are never alone (always connected to the universal consciousness, that is also within).

## Step 10 – The Return

As with all journeys into the subconscious I guide you back the way that you came (back along your meadow, along your light pathway, and returning through the gateway of your main fat cell, the same way you entered closing the gateway behind you and opening your eyes when ready). There are key visual pointers throughout the visualisation that you can use often on a daily basis, like clearing your negative thoughts / fears etc. with the weight box and filling with light, to the imagining of your connection to the highest source. They are excellent visual tools to keep replacing the old destructive neural pathways of the mind / emotion links to positive ones.

# 33
## SIMPLICITY FROM COMPLEXITY

I have endeavoured in this book to help those who choose to take part in *The Weigh Forward* programme to release themselves from hundreds of years of negative attitudes to food and body shape; to break the pattern of an increasingly 'outside' based society and, instead, deepen your intimate knowledge of yourself; to embrace rather than shy away from your emotional past and achieve lasting weight loss in the process.

In doing this you will hopefully have mastered skills that will help you become better equipped to deal with the challenges of everyday life. I say simplicity from complexity because I have shared complicated understandings of the subconscious, of the complex chemical and emotional mix of food and feelings. You have been asked to explore your thoughts, belief systems, use of language, and to discern information about your very DNA and cellular make-up to name but during this process.

However, the simplicity remains. Weight is a subconscious issue. By understanding the subconscious reason you were holding on to weight and the subsequent pattern you were running you can keep it simple from now on – by working with yourself in recognising what emotions are being triggered in times of destructive eating or weight gain, and reassuring yourself back into balance with your tools of affirmations, writing, visualisations and exercises.

Having explored the complexity, keep reiterating to yourself the simplicity, because you have cleared your core emotional block there is no longer a reason to hold on to weight.

Keep affirming you are 'letting go' or 'releasing' your protective layers of fat, eating with chemotional balance and participating in chemotional exercise. The subconscious will still try to lead you astray to some quick fix solution. Just smile at the early signs of sabotage and carry on with the tools you have. This is one of the reasons mind-programming tools such as 'tapping' won't work in the long run. You have to own and heal your emotional past, learning from it. Tapping and other forms of supposed emotional release are only temporary because the lesson hasn't been understood and, like an acupuncture release, you will pinpoint emotional discordance but not clear it. It also means that, in times of heightened emotional triggers, any thoughts of tapping go straight out of the window. Keep it simple, embrace the tools you have, because you have everything you need.

On a final note, society itself at present is on a chosen road that leads away from contemplation and self-responsibility.

In 2010, Nicholas Carr released his book, *The Shallows*, explaining how years of daily internet use is shaping the way his mind works. He said when he used to read:

> *'My mind would get caught up in the twists of the narrative, or the turns of the argument, and I'd spend hours strolling through long stretches of prose... Now my concentration starts to drift after a page or two. I get fidgety, lose the thread, and begin looking for something else to do. I feel as though I am always dragging my wayward brain back to the text.'*

His conclusion (and many other psychologists, neurobiologists and educators agree):

228

*'When you go online, you enter an environment that promotes cursory reading, hurried and distracted thinking and superficial learning. What the net diminishes is the ability to follow in-depth a subject for ourselves to construct within our minds the rich and idiosyncratic set of connections that give rise to a singular intelligence.'*

*The Weigh Forward* asks you to reclaim that calm, focused, undisturbed mind and remain able to embrace deep contemplation.

To paraphrase Vinnie Jones, 'It's been chemotional!'

229